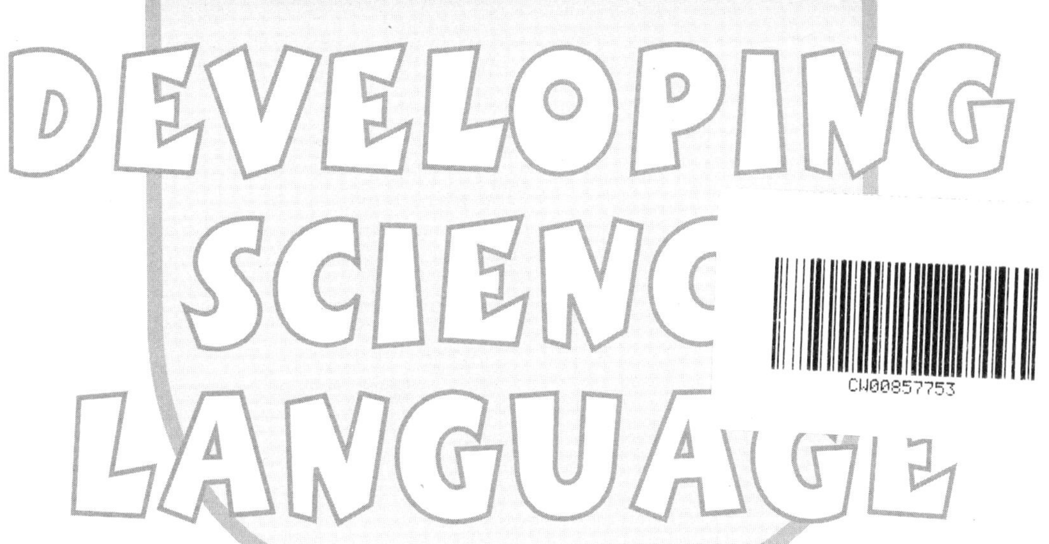

for

Materials

with

10–11

year olds

William Hartley

Published by Scholastic Ltd,
Villiers House,
Clarendon Avenue,
Leamington Spa,
Warwickshire CV32 5PR
Visit our website at www. scholastic.co.uk

Printed by Alden Group Ltd, Oxford

1 2 3 4 5 6 7 8 9 0 2 3 4 5 6 7 8 9 0 1

AUTHOR
William Hartley

LITERACY CONSULTANT
Gill Matthews

EDITOR
Joel Lane

ASSISTANT EDITOR
David Sandford

SERIES DESIGNER
Rachael Hammond

DESIGNER
Micky Pledge

COVER PHOTOGRAPH
© Stockbyte

ILLUSTRATIONS
The Drawing Room

British Library Cataloguing-in-Publication Data
A catalogue record for this book is available from the British Library.

ISBN 0-439-01881-1

Designed using Adobe Pagemaker

CONTENTS

CONTENTS

INTRODUCTION

Children often struggle to remember science words. Sometimes the words seem strange or unusual and sometimes the words we use in science have other meanings in everyday life. Think about these science words: *material, property, hard, soft.* If you ask a child what these words mean, you are likely to get responses such as: 'My coat is made of material'; 'My things are my property'; 'These sums are too hard for me'; 'You won't do that because you're soft'. But when children go into science lessons, we sometimes assume that they already understand a 'material' to be any substance, a 'property' to be how a material behaves, and 'hard' or 'soft' to be words that describe one of the many properties of a material.

Scientific language

This series aims to give children practice in using science words, both through science activities and in 'real life' contexts, so that they become familiar with the scientific meanings of these words. Use of the correct scientific vocabulary is essential for high attainment in SATs. The QCA *Scheme of Work for Science* (DfES) for Key Stages 1 and 2 in England suggests vocabulary for each of its units; although these books are not divided into exactly the same topics, the QCA vocabulary and its progressive introduction are used as the basis for the word selection here.

The science covered is divided into units based on topics from the national curricula for England, Wales, Scotland and Northern Ireland. In this book, the science is drawn from the 'Materials and their properties' statements for ages 10–11 relating to grouping materials and changing materials. The series of boxed letters at the bottom of each page shows in which curriculum documents the focus of each activity occurs. If all the boxes are shaded like this, E NI W S (as for example on page 68), this indicates that the activity focuses on a topic from the Scottish guidelines only.

Science and literacy

The National Literacy Strategy for England suggests teaching objectives and gives examples of the types of activities that children should encounter during each year of primary school. This book uses many of these techniques for developing children's understanding and use of scientific language. The activities here are mainly intended for use in science time, as they have been written with science learning objectives in mind. However, some of the activities could be used in literacy time. Science texts have already been published for use in literacy time, but many of them use science content appropriate for older children.

During literacy time you need to be focusing on language skills, not teaching new science. It is with this in mind that these sheets, drawing from age-appropriate science work, have been produced. It is also suggested that these sheets are used in literacy time only after the science content has been introduced in science time.

The series focuses mainly on paper-based activities to develop scientific language, rather than experimental and investigative work, but it is hoped that teachers might use some of the ideas in planning practical science activities.

About this book

Each unit in this book begins with a non-fiction text that introduces some key scientific vocabulary. The key words are highlighted by bold type. The texts cover a range of non-fiction genres. Following this text are two comprehension activities that help children to identify and understand the key words (and introduce some new science words). There are two levels:

 for older or more able children

 for younger or less able children.

Although the comprehension activities are designed to be used mainly during science time, you may wish to use the texts as examples of non-fiction texts in literacy time. The comprehension pages contain two or three types of question (a change of icon indicates a change in the type of question):

 The answer can be found in the text.

 Children will need to think about the answer. These questions usually elicit science understanding beyond what the text provides.

 An activity aimed at developing the children's broader skills. These are optional extension activities for individual or group work, with teacher support if necessary.

Following the comprehension pages in each unit are activities aimed at developing children's understanding and use of the key vocabulary. Strategies used include: making and completing diagrams, charts and tables; description; labelling; sequencing; analysing graphs and tables; matching sentence starters to endings; identifying true and false statements; wordsearches; vocabulary games and quizzes; and some easily set up practical activities.

WORD LIST

abrasion
air
air spaces
alloy
aluminium
appearance
approximate
atmosphere

boil
boiling point
boulder
brass
brick
bronze
burning

ceramic
chalk
change of state
china
clay
cloud
coal
coke
compare
concrete
condense
contract
contraction
copper
crude oil
crust

decompose
degrees Celsius
dissolve
dredging
drilling
droplet
durable

electrical conductor
electrical insulator
environment
evaporate
evaporation
exhale
expand
expansion
experiment

fabric
fall
fibre
filter paper
flexibility
flexible
fossil
fossil fuel
freeze
freezing point
funnel

gas
glass
granite
graph
gravel
grit

hail
hard
heat resistance
humus

ice
igneous
incinerated
ingredient
insoluble
irreversible

landfill
light
limestone
liquid

malleable
marble
matter
measure
measurement
melting
metal
metamorphic
mineral
mining
mixture
moulded

natural gas
nylon

observations
oil
ore

paraffin
particle
pebble
permeability
petrol
plastic
precipitation
process
property
pure

quarrying
quartz

rain
recording
recover
recycled
reused
reversible
rise
rubber
rubbish
rust

salt
sand
sedimentary
seep
separate
shape
shock
sieve
slate
sleet
snow
soak
soft
soil
solid
soluble
solute
solution
solvent
state
steam
steel
stone
strength
strong
substance
suspension

temperature
texture
thermal conductor
thermal insulator
thermometer
tile
tin
toxic
transparent
transpire

volume

waste
water
water cycle
water vapour
wood
wool

zinc

Comparing and using materials

In our science class, we have been looking at the similarities and differences between materials. We looked at materials commonly found in houses. We thought about their **properties**, and how they are used.

Wood is **hard** and **strong**. It can be used to construct doors, floorboards and furniture.

Plastic is **light** in weight. It combines **strength** and **flexibility**. This means that it is ideal for washing-up bowls, window frames and other **moulded** items. Plastic is also a good **electrical** and **thermal insulator**. It can therefore be used to cover electric cables in order to reduce the risk of getting an electric shock. When used to cover saucepan handles, plastic helps to protect hands from getting burnt.

Glass is **transparent**. This makes it a suitable material for windows. It can be stretched into thin **fibres**. In a bundle, these fibres trap air and make a good **thermal insulator**. Glass fibres are used for loft insulation.

Most **metals** are **hard** and **strong**, but are also **malleable**. This means that they can easily be hammered or pressed into shape. All of these features make metals the ideal material for water pipes, radiators, pans and household tools (such as hammers and saws).

Fabrics are **soft** and **flexible**, and are available in a wide range of colours. They are the obvious material for curtains, furniture covers and clothes.

Finally, there are **ceramic** materials. These have been made by baking clay or a similar material. Ceramic materials are used for crockery (**china**), ovenware (Pyrex), walls (**brick**) and doorsteps (**concrete**), because of their **strength**, **heat resistance** and resistance to **abrasion**.

We were really quite amazed at how many different properties a material possesses, and what it can be used for. We also realised that a particular job can often be done by more than one type of material.

Comparing and using materials

1. Why is **wood** used to construct doors, floorboards and furniture?

2. Why is **glass** suitable for windows?

3. Name three properties common to most **metals**.

4. Name three properties common to most **ceramics**.

5. **Plastic** is a good **electrical insulator**. What risk does covering electrical cables with **plastic** help to reduce?

6. **Plastic** is also a good **thermal insulator**. What does covering a saucepan handle with **plastic** help to prevent?

7. Which properties of **metals** make them suitable for making water pipes, radiators and tools such as hammers and saws?

8. What does this sentence mean? '**Plastic** can easily be **moulded**'.

9. On another sheet of paper, write the names of two household objects not named in the text that can be made from:

a) wood **b)** glass **c)** metal

10. Write the meanings of these words on another sheet of paper:

transparent malleable flexible abrasion

Choose five objects in your classroom. Talk with a friend about the properties of the material from which each object is made. Write the names of other materials that could be used to make each object. Explain why each material would be suitable for the job.

Comparing and using materials

1. Complete these sentences.

a) **Wood** is ________ and ___________, and can be used to make doors, floorboards and furniture.

b) **Plastic** is _________ in weight and combines

_______________ with ____________________ .

c) **Glass** is ____________, and is also a good ____________ ____________

2. Circle 'True' or 'False'.
a) Most metals are **hard, strong** and **malleable**. **True / False**

b) **Fabrics** are **transparent** and are available in many colours. **True / False**

3. **Plastic** is a good **electrical insulator**. What risk does covering electrical cables with plastic help to reduce?

____

4. Which material is used to make radiators and saucepans? ______________________________

5. Tick the objects that are made from fabric.

crockery | curtains | concrete
furniture covers | pliers | clothes

6. Why does covering a saucepan handle with **plastic** help to protect hands from being burnt? Write your answer on the back of the sheet.

7. Write the name of one other household item made from:

a) wood ____________ **b)** glass ____________ **c)** metal ____________

8. Write the meanings of these words on a separate piece of paper:

transparent   malleable   flexible

Choose one classroom object. Discuss the properties of the material from which it is made with a friend. Use descriptive words such as **hard, soft, flexible** and **rigid**. Write the names of other materials that could be used to make the same object.

Forceful changes

This wordsearch contains the names of ten different **forces** that can act on a material. All the words end in '**ing**'.
To help you find each word, a written clue, a picture clue and the first letter are given below.
Be careful! Some of the words have similar meanings.
You will have to search in all directions, including diagonally.
Draw a line through each word in the wordsearch when you find it.

Clues

1. Pushing hard on something. **(p)**
2. Bending or coiling into a spiral. **(c)**
3. Getting smaller, especially as a result of getting wet. **(s)**
4. Forcing something into a curve. **(b)**
5. Pushing hard on something and breaking it. **(c)**
6. Becoming smaller when cooled. **(c)**
7. Pulling something out into a greater length. **(s)**
8. Becoming larger when heated. **(e)**
9. Changing the shape of something by turning one end. **(t)**
10. Pushing hard on something and compressing it. **(s)**

g	n	i	h	c	t	e	r	t	s	l	e
q	a	c	c	t	y	p	p	c	g	g	x
z	d	o	g	e	w	n	h	b	n	n	p
g	o	n	b	z	o	i	w	i	f	y	a
n	f	t	g	n	i	h	s	u	r	c	n
i	s	r	r	l	a	s	l	t	e	m	d
h	k	a	v	g	e	e	t	s	i	m	i
s	k	c	u	r	l	i	n	g	d	n	n
a	b	t	p	v	b	e	n	d	i	n	g
u	r	i	x	i	d	c	h	a	u	i	f
q	k	n	q	x	j	t	w	j	h	u	i
s	j	g	s	h	r	i	n	k	i	n	g

Choose three of the words that you have found. On the back of this sheet, use each word correctly in a separate sentence to describe someone changing the shape of a material.

True or false?

Use a ruler to underline the sentence in each pair that is **true**.

1. A **brittle** material will snap or break more easily than a material that is **flexible**.
An **opaque** object lets light pass through it.

2. **Translucent** materials let more light pass through them than **transparent** materials.
A **waterproof** surface is resistant to water.

3. Copper is a **ductile** metal that can be drawn out into fine strands to make wires.
A **permeable** material does not allow water to pass through it.

4. **Luminous** materials will glow in the dark.
Feathers make poor cushion fillers because they are **soft** and **squashable**.

5. An **absorbent** material is not a good choice for soaking up spilt liquid.
Clay is **amorphous** but baked clay has a definite shape.

6. Scent is normally **odourless**.
Glass is used for windows because it is **smooth**, **strong** and **transparent**.

7. The way a material feels is called its **texture**.
A **porous** material is completely waterproof.

8. **Reflective** surfaces do not show up well in the beam of a torch.
A metal pole is **firm** and **rigid**, but a pillow is **soft** and **squashable**.

9. **Viscous** liquids are thin and runny.
Rust causes certain metals to **corrode**.

10. **Similar** objects can often be manufactured from **different** materials.
The **appearance** of a material is the way that it smells.

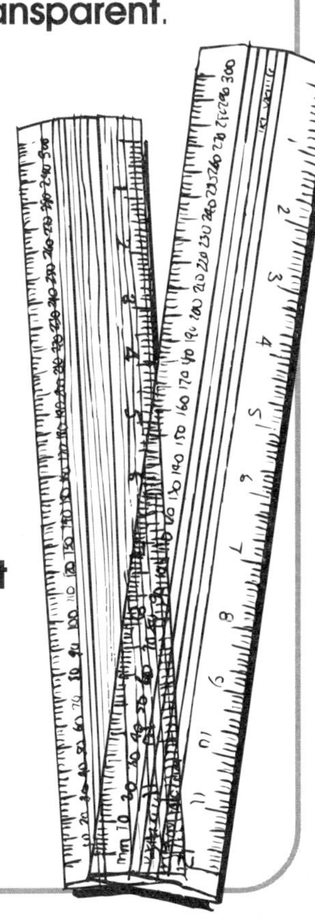

On a separate sheet of paper, rewrite the sentences that are **false** to make them **true**.

Building materials

On this drawing of a house are the names of some **materials** used in its construction. Look carefully to see where each kind of material is used, then answer the questions on the sheet 'Building materials 2'.

Building materials 2

Use the sheet 'Building materials 1' to help you answer these questions.

1. The labelled materials on the picture of the house all have special **properties** that make them suitable for the job they do.
Name three such properties for each material listed below. One material has already been done for you.

slate	steel	mortar	glass
rigid			
waterproof			
flat			

wood	concrete	brick	plastic

2. With the exception of **glass** and **mortar**, all the materials labelled on the drawing could be replaced by alternative materials that would do the job just as well.
Write the name of one alternative material that could be used in place of each of the materials listed below.

slate	steel	stone	brick
wood	**aluminium**	**concrete**	**plastic**

3. Talk with a friend about the materials used to **manufacture** a car. On another sheet of paper, draw a car and label the main materials that it contains.

Choosing materials

Cross out the **properties** that are not correct for each **material**.
Use a dictionary to look up the meanings of any words you don't know.

IRON
firm
soft
bendy amorphous
solid dull

NATURAL SPONGE
soft
manufactured firm
absorbent tough
porous

WOOD
bouncy
flexible hard
solid opaque
luminous

ROCK
reflective
dull rough
translucent rigid
fluid

PLASTIC
malleable
waterproof edible
brittle squashy
flexible

GLASS
transparent
viscous smooth
hard shiny
rigid

WATER
liquid
ductile stiff
opaque hard
transparent

RUBBER
flexible
bendy heatproof
natural smooth
soft

PUTTY
permeable
natural strong
squashable elastic
amorphous

LUBRICATING OIL
smelly
translucent stiff
water-absorbent
fluid liquid

Recycling is important

The problem

Almost all areas of human activity produce **waste** of one kind or another.
The amount of **waste** and **rubbish** produced by different countries in the world varies enormously. In Britain alone, it is estimated that enough domestic rubbish is produced daily to fill Trafalgar Square to the top of Nelson's Column.

What happens to all this rubbish?

Most of it is taken away by local refuse collectors. It is then either **incinerated** or dumped in large **landfill** sites. These sites are eventually covered over with topsoil. Trees and shrubs are then often planted to provide wildlife habitats and recreational areas.

Is this a sensible way to deal with waste and rubbish?

Not really: both of these methods cause problems. **Burning** waste produces poisonous fumes. Burying it results in some of the waste products remaining in the ground for a long time. As the products slowly **decompose** they release **toxic** substances into the surrounding soil. These substances **seep** into streams and rivers and cause damage to the natural **environment**.

What is the alternative?

Many products can be **reused** (milk bottles, for example) or **recycled**. Glass, metal cans, plastic bottles, paper and cardboard are all readily recyclable materials. These products account for about 40 per cent of the mass of rubbish thrown out by the average family in a year.
Just imagine the reduction in environmental damage and the money that could be saved if this quantity of waste material could be used again, instead of being either incinerated or dumped into a landfill site. In the interests of the future, recycling makes sense.

Recycling is important

1. What is the main problem created by almost all kinds of human activity?

____

2. Name the two most common ways of getting rid of domestic **rubbish**.

_______________ _______________

3. What would be reduced if the majority of household waste were either **reused** or **recycled**?

____

4. Which materials account for about 40 per cent of the mass of **rubbish** thrown out by the average family in a year?

____

Answer questions 5, 7 and 9 on another sheet of paper.

5. What are the main problems created by the two main ways in which Britain gets rid of its **rubbish**?

6. Write a definition for each of these words:

domestic incinerate decompose toxic seep

7. Glass milk bottles are **reusable**. Name some other products that can be used again after being cleaned.

8. Circle the word that describes glass, metal cans, plastic bottles, paper and cardboard.

natural biodegradable recyclable intoxicating

9. Write the names of two other recyclable materials not mentioned in the text.

Almost one-third of domestic **rubbish** comes from packaging of different kinds. Paper, cardboard, glass, metal and plastic are all used for packaging. For one week, make a daily list of the packaging that you and your household throw away. Which of the things on your list could be **recycled** at a local recycling centre?

Recycling is important

1. What do almost all areas of human activity produce?

____

2. Tick the two most common ways of getting rid of domestic **rubbish**.

recycling	☐	dumping in landfill sites	☐	reusing	☐
reclaiming	☐	incinerating	☐	restoring	☐

3. Complete these sentences.

a) Burning waste produces ________________ fumes.

b) Burying ________________ results in some of the waste products remaining in the ________________ for a long time.

4. What do waste products release into the surrounding soil as they slowly **decompose**? ________________

5. Name one product that can be **reused**. ________________

6. Name five materials that can be **recycled**. ________________

____

7. Write two things that are likely to happen if we don't try to **recycle** as many of our waste products as possible.

____

____

8. How could you reuse some of your classroom items such as yoghurt pots, newspaper and packaging?

____

Almost one-third of domestic **rubbish** comes from packaging of different kinds. Paper, cardboard, glass, metal and plastic are all used for packaging. With your friends, make a list each day for a week of the types of material thrown away in your classroom. Which of the things on your list could be **recycled** at a local recycling centre?

Recycling in action

1. Decide which recycling bank each type of waste should go into. One has been done for you.

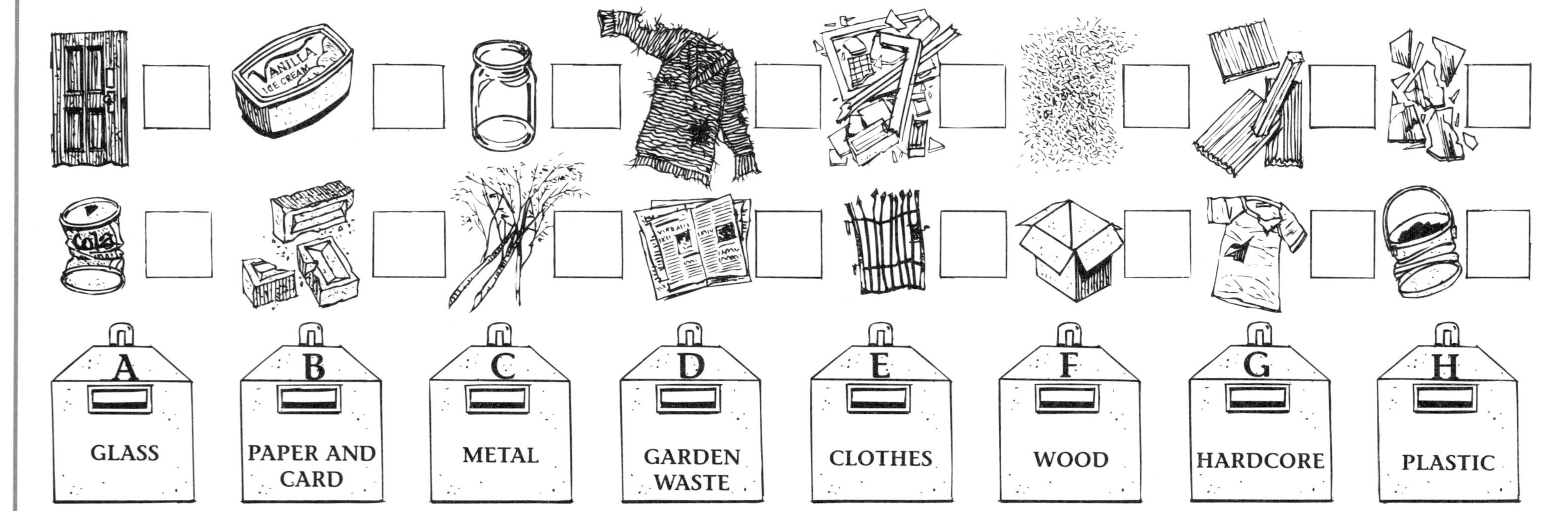

2. Which of the following are benefits of recycling? Write down the ones you choose to complete the sentence.

- conserves natural resources
- increases pollution
- reduces the need for landfill space
- saves energy in production and transport
- uses up more of the world's resources
- reduces the risk of pollution
- encourages people to waste more
- reduces the amount of toxic fumes discharged by waste incinerators

Recycling makes sense because it ____________________

Mixtures

Some materials are **pure**. They are made from one **substance**. Iron, aluminium, oxygen and nitrogen are materials that are pure. Most materials are **mixtures**. They are made from two or more different substances mixed together.

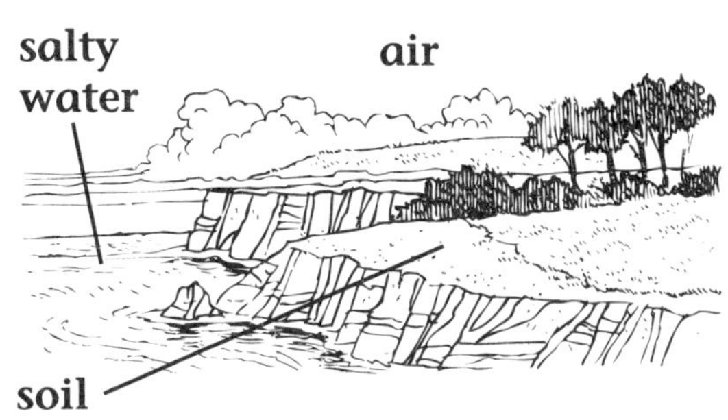

Air, salty water and soil are mixtures. Air is a mixture of gases: oxygen, nitrogen, carbon dioxide, water vapour and small amounts of some other gases. Salty water is a mixture of salt and water. Soil is a mixture of sand, clay, humus, water and air. Sometimes the materials that make up mixtures are also mixtures themselves. The air in soil is an example of this.

Mixing substances can create new materials that have different **properties** from the original substances, and so may have a wider range of uses.

For example, if two metals are melted down and the resulting liquids are mixed together, an **alloy** is produced. **Bronze** is an alloy of **copper** and **tin**. **Brass** is an alloy of **copper** and **zinc**. Bronze and brass possess many of the properties of copper, but are much harder and more **durable** than copper on its own.

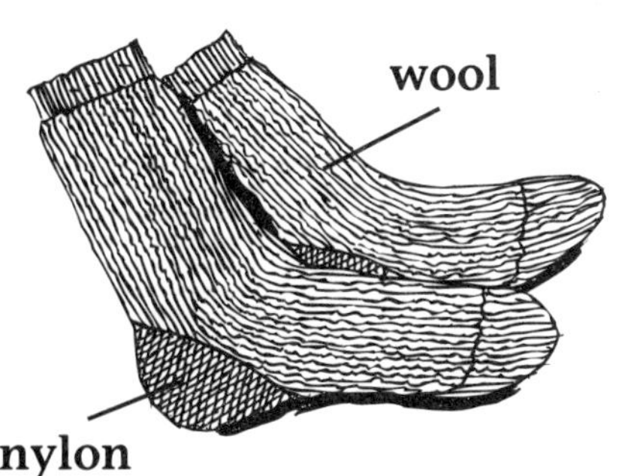

Sometimes materials can be mixed simply by using them together to combine some of the properties of each material. For example, most socks are manufactured by weaving together **wool** and **nylon**. This combines the softness of wool with the **strength** of nylon.

Most foods are a mixture of substances. The different substances are called **ingredients**. The different ingredients give each food its colour, flavour and **texture**.

Mixtures

1. Name four **pure** materials.

______________ ______________ ______________ ______________

2. What is a material called if it is made from two or more different **substances**? ______________

Air is a **mixture** of which **substances**?

____

3. Mixing **substances** together can sometimes create new materials. How are these new materials often different from the original **substances** from which they were made?

____

____

4. Name the five main substances that make up **soil**. ______________

____

Answer questions 5, 6 and 7 on another sheet of paper.

5. How is an **alloy** formed?

6. What is: **a) bronze**? **b) brass**? Write each answer as a short sentence.

7. Write the meaning of each of these words: **a) durable** and **b) ingredient**.

8. Concrete is a mixture of different things. Write the names of the things that are used to make concrete.

____

9. Use science reference books and other sources to help you find out what each of these materials is made from.

a) water ______________ **b)** sugar ______________

Most foods are a mixture of many **ingredients**. Use food packets and labels to find out the main ingredients in a range of different food products. Record your results on a chart for display in the classroom.

Mixtures

1. Name two **pure** materials and two materials that are **mixtures**.

pure material		mixture of materials	

2. Choose the correct words from the box below to fill in this sentence.

Air is a mixture of ______________, ______________, carbon dioxide,

______________ ______________ and small amounts of some other gases.

water vapour	neon	helium	nitrogen
oxygen	water drops	hydro-electric	hydrogen

3. What is the common name for a **mixture** of sand, clay, humus, water and air? ______________

4. Circle the two things that most socks are likely to be a **mixture** of.

leather nylon silk wool fur

5. Cross out the words that are wrong in each sentence.

a) **Bronze** is an **alloy** of **iron / copper** and **tin / zinc**.

b) **Brass** is an **alloy** of **copper / gold** and **silver / zinc**.

6. Are **bronze** and **brass** harder or softer than **copper**? ______________

7. What are the different substances in food called? ______________

8. Concrete is a mixture of different things. Find out what. Tick the things most likely to be found in some concrete.

sand	☐	salt	☐	cement	☐
chalk	☐	gravel	☐	soil	☐

Most foods are a mixture of many **ingredients**. Use food packets and labels to find out the main ingredients in a range of different food products. Write down some of the names of ingredients you find.

Clothing mixtures

The **fibres** used to make **fabrics** for clothing can be either **natural** or **synthetic**. Each type of fabric has different properties, which clothing manufacturers have to consider when deciding which fibres to mix for a certain item of clothing.

Natural fibres such as **wool** and **cotton** make fabrics that are comfortable to wear next to your skin, but are not particularly strong or long-lasting. Fabrics made from synthetic fibres, such as **nylon** and **polyester**, are not as comfortable to wear, but are much stronger and last longer than natural fibres.

Mixing natural and synthetic fibres together can produce fabrics that are comfortable, strong and long-lasting.

1. Look at the labels on different clothes to find out what each garment is made from. Write your results on the chart. An example has been done for you. You may find that some garments contain only one kind of fibre.

garment	fibre/s	natural/synthetic/mixture
sweatshirt	cotton, polyester	mixture

2. Which **fabric** seems most popular in the making of clothes? ______________________

3. Name the garments that were made entirely from:

a) **natural** fibres ______________________

b) **synthetic** fibres ______________________

4. Which garments were a **mixture** of natural and synthetic fibres?

____

Edible mixtures

Most food products are a **mixture** of many different **substances**. The different substances found in food are called **ingredients**. Some of the ingredients in food products will be familiar to you. There are others that you have probably never heard of!

1. Look at some empty food packets to find out which **ingredients** each food contains. Write your results in the boxes below. The first one has been done for you.

Food name	Food name	Food name	Food name
corn flakes			
Main ingredients	**Main ingredients**	**Main ingredients**	**Main ingredients**
maize, sugar, malt flavouring, salt, niacin, iron, vitamins			

Food name	Food name	Food name	Food name
Main ingredients	**Main ingredients**	**Main ingredients**	**Main ingredients**

2. Which **ingredient** occurred in more of the food products than any other? ____________________

3. Write the names of some food products that had sugar in them.

____

4. Choose **two** ingredients that you have never heard of. Use reference books, CD-ROMs or the Internet to find out what they are and why they are in your food. Write down their names and uses on another sheet.

Mixing with water

Some solids will **dissolve** when mixed with water. When this happens, the solid breaks up into tiny **particles** – so small that you cannot see them. Water containing a dissolved solid is called a **solution**.

Some solids will not dissolve when mixed with water. They can usually still be seen in the water. After a while, some will either sink to the bottom or float to the top. Others will stay in **suspension**, spread evenly throughout the water.

Do this experiment.
You will need: four clear plastic containers full of water, a stopwatch, a tablespoon, a sheet of drawing paper and a pencil. You will also need: samples of four materials: sand, soil, table salt and sawdust.

What to do:
1. Stir a tablespoon of one of the materials into one of the containers.
2. Continue stirring for 30 seconds.
3. Watch what happens to the mixture for 5 minutes.
4. On your sheet of paper, draw what the mixture looks like after 5 minutes. Write a caption to explain what has happened. The picture on the right shows an example.
5. Repeat steps 1 to 4 for the other three materials.

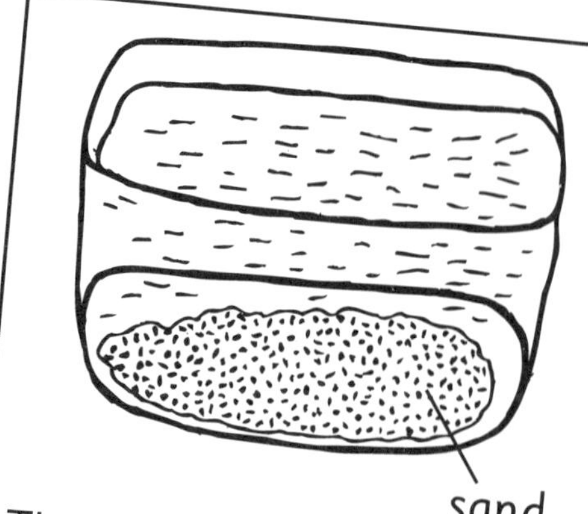

sand
The sand has sunk to the bottom of the container and left the water looking clear and pure.

On your sheet of paper, answer these questions. Write in full sentences.
1. What happened to the salt when it was mixed with the water?
2. What is water containing a dissolved solid known as?
3. Which materials in the soil:
a) sink? **b)** float? **c)** remain in **suspension**?

Separating methods

Lorraine and Zaheed read these instructions on a page of their science textbook before carrying out some experiments on separating materials.

● How to **separate** a **mixture** of sugar and dried rice

You will need: a mixture of sugar and rice, a **sieve**, two empty cups.

What to do:

1. Rest sieve on top of cup.
2. Pour mixture into sieve.
3. Gently shake sieve.
4. Tip rice from sieve into empty cup.

The sugar and the rice have now been separated.

● How to **separate** a **mixture** of sand and water

You will need: a stirred mixture of sand and water, a plastic bottle, a **funnel**, a saucer, a sheet of **filter paper**.

What to do:

1. Place funnel in neck of bottle.
2. Put filter paper in funnel.
3. Pour mixture into funnel.
4. Tip sand off filter paper onto saucer.

The sand and the water have now been separated.

● How to **recover** salt from a salt **solution**

You will need: a salt solution in a saucer.

What to do:

Leave mixture to stand near a warm radiator until only the salt remains.

The salt has now been separated from the water.

MESSING ABOUT WITH SCIENCE Book 4

Separating methods

1. What equipment is required to **separate** a **mixture** of sugar and dried rice?

____

2. Here are the instructions for separating a **mixture** of sugar and dried rice. Write the letters A to D in the boxes to show the correct sequence.

A. Pour mixture into sieve.
B. Tip rice from sieve into empty cup.
C. Rest sieve on top of cup.
D. Gently shake sieve.

☐ ☐ ☐ ☐

3. Which experiment on page 59 of *MESSING ABOUT WITH SCIENCE Book 4* uses both **filter paper** and a **funnel**?

____

4. How would you **recover** the salt from a salt **solution**?

____

____

5. Describe the appearance of a **sieve**.

____

____

6. Explain what might happen in the first experiment if the gaps in the **sieve** were too large.

____

7. What is the purpose of the **filter paper** in the second experiment?

____

8. What do you think happened to the water in the salt **solution** when the **mixture** was left to stand near a warm radiator?

____

How would you **separate** a **mixture** of flour and currants? What equipment would you use? Add diagrams to your explanation.

Separating methods

1. Tick the items of equipment needed to **separate** a **mixture** of sugar and dried rice.

saucer ☐ sieve ☐ funnel ☐

cups ☐ filter paper ☐ bottle ☐

2. Write the letters A to D to show the correct sequence of pictures.

_______ _______ _______ _______

3. Write the missing words in these instructions for separating a **mixture** of sand and water.

a) Place _______________ in neck of bottle.

b) Put _______________ paper into funnel.

c) Pour _______________ into funnel.

d) Tip sand off filter paper onto _______________ .

4. Cross out the words that are wrong in this sentence.
To recover salt from a salt **situation / solution**, leave the mixture to stand near a **warm / cold** radiator until only the **water / salt** remains.

5. Name each of these items.

_______________ _______________ _______________

6. In the second experiment on page 59 of the science textbook, why does the sand not pass through the **filter paper** into the bottle?

____

7. Circle the materials that are found in a salt **solution**.

sand water sugar salt rice

Explain how to **separate** a mixture of flour and currants. (Hint: look at the first experiment on page 59 of *MESSING ABOUT WITH SCIENCE Book 4*.)

Sieving

A **sieve** can be used to **separate** either a **mixture** of solids or a mixture of a solid and a liquid. When a mixture of solids is placed in a **sieve**, the smaller particles fall through the **mesh** of holes and the larger particles are trapped in the sieve.

Sometimes a type of sieve called a **colander** is used in the kitchen to separate food items, such as peas or carrots, from the water in which they have been cooked. The holes in the colander allow the water to pass through, but not the solids.

1. Describe how you would **separate** a **mixture** of fine soil and pebbles.

2. How could you separate cabbage from its cooking water?

3. Swap **two** words round in each sentence in this passage, then rewrite the passage so that it makes complete sense.

A sieve will different a mixture of solids of separate sizes. It is a round wire holding a frame net. Small holes can pass through the solids, but larger ones cannot.

4. On another sheet of paper, explain how a fishing boat can use different nets to control the size of fish that are caught.

Filtering

When a **solid** such as sand is mixed with water, the sand can be **separated** from the water by **filtering**. Filtering is a simple **process**, very like using a sieve. It is carried out using the **method** shown in the **diagram** on the right.

When the **mixture** is poured onto the folded **filter paper** fitted in the filter **funnel**, the paper traps the sand but allows the water to pass through it. The sand becomes a **residue** and the water becomes a **filtrate**. This happens because the filter paper is **porous**. A material that is porous lets **liquids** and **gases** pass through it, but not **solids**.

1. Write the meanings of these words:

a) residue ______________________________

____

b) filtrate ______________________________

____

2. Tick the items that are made from porous materials.

cotton cloth	☐	glass tumbler	☐	gauze bandage	☐
aluminium can	☐	paper towel	☐	plastic bottle	☐
stick of chalk	☐	polythene sheet	☐	blotting paper	☐

3. Explain in writing how to filter a mixture of water and clay using a plastic bottle, a filter funnel and some filter paper. Include a diagram with your explanation. Try to use the words in the word bank below.

porous	solid	liquid	separate	filtrate	residue

Evaporation

Water is changing into **water vapour** all the time. We call this change **evaporation**. When water **evaporates** it changes from a **liquid** to a **gas**. The warmer the water is, the more quickly it evaporates. When water reaches its **boiling** point, a **temperature** of 100°C, it starts to **boil**. Boiling water is evaporating as quickly as it can.

Some of the water vapour in the air comes from living things. Living plants and animals consist mainly of water. Some of this water evaporates from the surface of plants and animals.

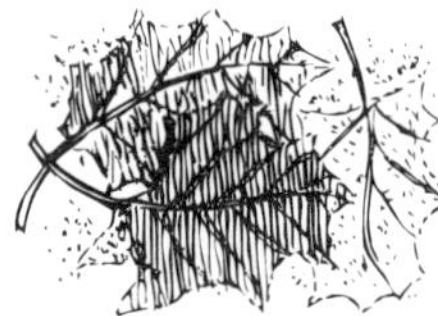

Some of the water vapour in the air comes from dead plants and animals. When water evaporates from dead plants and animals, they dry up.

Most of the water vapour in the air comes from **mixtures** that contain water, but have never been alive. When water evaporates from these, the rest of the mixture is left behind. This is why dry mud remains when a puddle evaporates, or salt is left when sea water evaporates.

Record ten key facts from the passage above, in the same order.

1. Water is evaporating all the time.
2. __________
3. __________
4. __________
5. __________
6. __________
7. __________
8. __________
9. __________
10. __________

Magnetic separation

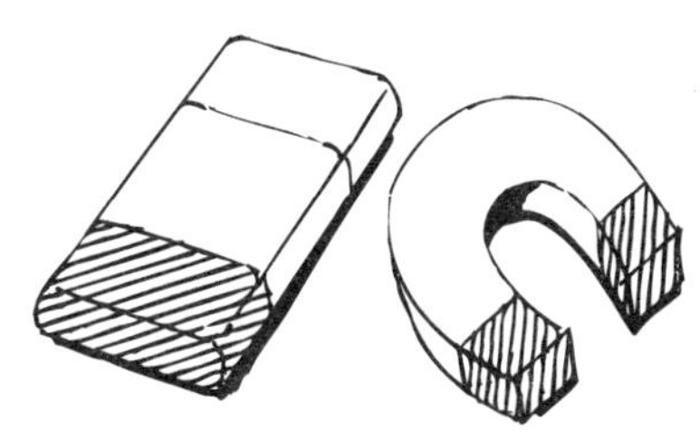

Sieving, **filtering** and **evaporating** are all simple methods of separating different mixtures of materials. Another way is to use a **magnet**. This will allow you to sort out **magnetic** from **non-magnetic** materials. Carry out this investigation.

You will need: a magnet and the objects listed on the chart below.

What to do: Test each object with the magnet and fill in the chart, then answer the questions below.

Object	Magnetic or non-magnetic?	Material it is made from
safety pin		
30cm ruler		
foil		
drawing pin		
paper clip		
scissors		
pencil		
chalk		
staples		
bulldog clip		
needle		
Plasticine		
tin lid		
1p coin		

1. Were all the objects with **metal** in them **magnetic**? ____________________

2. What do **metal** objects have to be made from to be **magnetic**?

____

3. Name four **metals** that are **not magnetic**.

____

4. **Test** other classroom objects with the magnet. Try to **predict** what will happen before you put the magnet next to each one. On another sheet of paper, make a list of the objects you tested that contained some **magnetic** material.

Missing words

Complete this page of instructions by writing in the words that are missing. They are all in the word bank at the bottom of the page. You may find it useful to have a dictionary handy!

CREATING AND SEPARATING A MIXTURE

Creating a mixture

Stir a tablespoon of salt into a jam jar half-full of warm water. The salt will ______________ in the water to form a salt solution. Now add a tablespoon of sand to the ______________ and stir well. The sand does not dissolve, because it is ______________. The particles of sand remain scattered in the salt solution. We say that the sand particles are in ______________ . These ______________ of sand will eventually sink to the bottom of the jar.

Separating the sand from the mixture

The sand can be separated from the mixture by a process called ______________. Put the stem of a filter funnel into the neck of a clean plastic bottle. Place a piece of folded ______________ paper in the bowl of the funnel. Pour the mixture through the filter paper. The filter paper traps the sand. The sand is called the ______________. The salt solution, known as the ______________, collects in the bottle.

Separating the salt from the mixture

Pour the salt solution onto a metal baking tray. Place the tray in the ______________ part of your classroom and leave it to stand until all the water has ______________. This may take ______________ days. Once the water has all gone, you will find only the salt remaining in the tray.

particles filtrate several dissolve filtration insoluble
filter evaporated suspension warmest residue solution

Heating and cooling

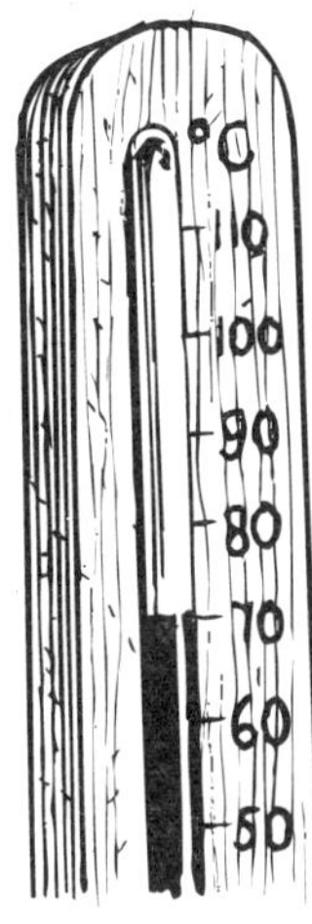

The **temperature** of a material is measured in **degrees Celsius (°C)** using a **thermometer**.

A change in temperature takes place if a material is either heated or cooled. An increase in temperature can cause a material to **expand**, becoming slightly bigger. A decrease in temperature can cause a material to **contract**, becoming slightly smaller.

Engineers have to allow for the **expansion** and **contraction** of materials in the buildings and structures all around us. For example, they string electric power cables loosely between their supports, so that the cables do not snap when they contract in cold weather.

A material may also go through a **change of state** when it is heated or cooled.

- An increase in temperature can change a **solid** into a **liquid**. This happens to chocolate when it is heated. It melts.
- An increase in temperature can also change a **liquid** into a **gas**. This happens to water when it reaches its **boiling point**. It changes into **water vapour**.

- A decrease in temperature can change a **gas** into a **liquid**. This happens to **water vapour** when it is cooled. It **condenses** and changes into water. In the air, condensing water vapour forms tiny droplets of **steam**.
- A decrease in temperature can also change a **liquid** into a **solid**. This happens to water when it reaches its **freezing point**. It freezes and changes into ice.

Heating and cooling

1. Name the instrument used for measuring temperature.

____

2. What must happen to a material to make its temperature change?

____

3. What happens to a material when it:

a) **expands**? ____

b) **contracts**? ____

4. Give one example of a situation where engineers have to allow for the **expansion** and **contraction** of materials.

____

____

5. What can an increase in temperature do to:

a) a **solid**? ____________________

____

b) a **liquid**? ____________________

____

6. What can a decrease in temperature do to:

a) a **gas**? ____________________

____

b) a **liquid**? ____________________

____

7. Which temperature scale is most commonly used on a **thermometer**? __________________________

8. What does it mean to say that a material is going through a **change of state**?

____

____

9. At what temperature does water: **a)** boil? ______°C **b)** freeze? ______°C

Make labelled diagrams to show what happens to **butter** and **wax** when they are heated and then allowed to cool down. Use reference books or CD-ROMs to find the names of other materials that will melt easily when heated.

Heating and cooling

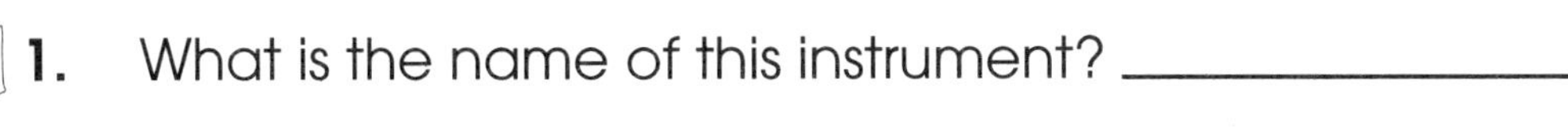

1. What is the name of this instrument? ______________________

2. Use the text to help you fill in the missing words in this sentence.

A change in ______________________ happens when a material

is either ______________________ or______________________.

3. Cross out the incorrect word in each of these sentences.
a) An **increase / decrease** in temperature can cause a material to expand.
b) An **increase / decrease** in temperature can cause a material to contract.

4. What would happen to electric power cables in cold weather if they were not strung loosely between their supports?

____

5. **a)** What happens to chocolate when it is heated?______________________

b) What does water become when it boils?______________________

6. **a)** What happens to water vapour when it cools?______________________

b) What does water become when it freezes?______________________

7. Which temperature scale is normally used on a **thermometer**?______________________

8. Choose one word from the list below to write in each empty box so that the statement makes sense.

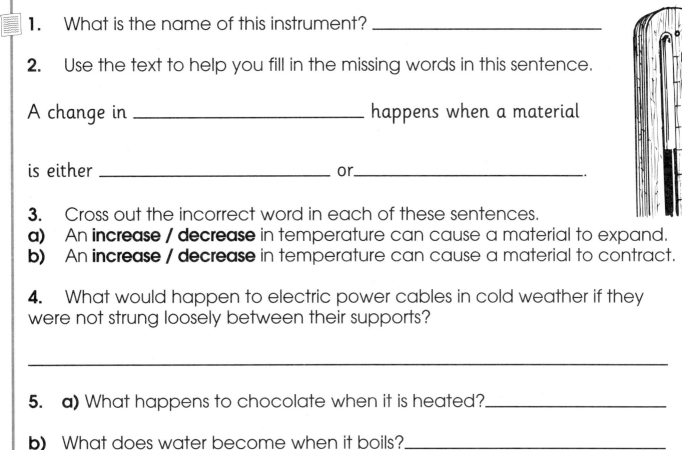

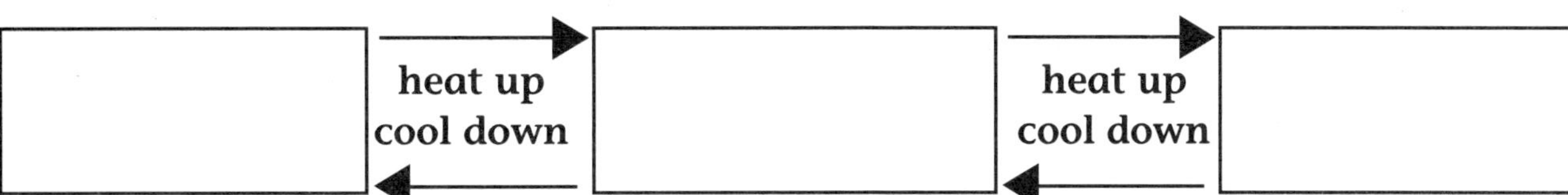

water stream ice lemonade steam rice

Draw a series of pictures to show what happens to **butter** when it is heated and then allowed to cool down. Write a caption under each picture.

Temperature word grid

All of these words are connected with **heating** and **cooling**.
Write each word on the grid in its correct place.

freeze	contract	heat	frozen
thermometer	cool	temperature	frost
cold	evaporate	expand	melt
boil	hot	radiator	warm
Celsius	condense		

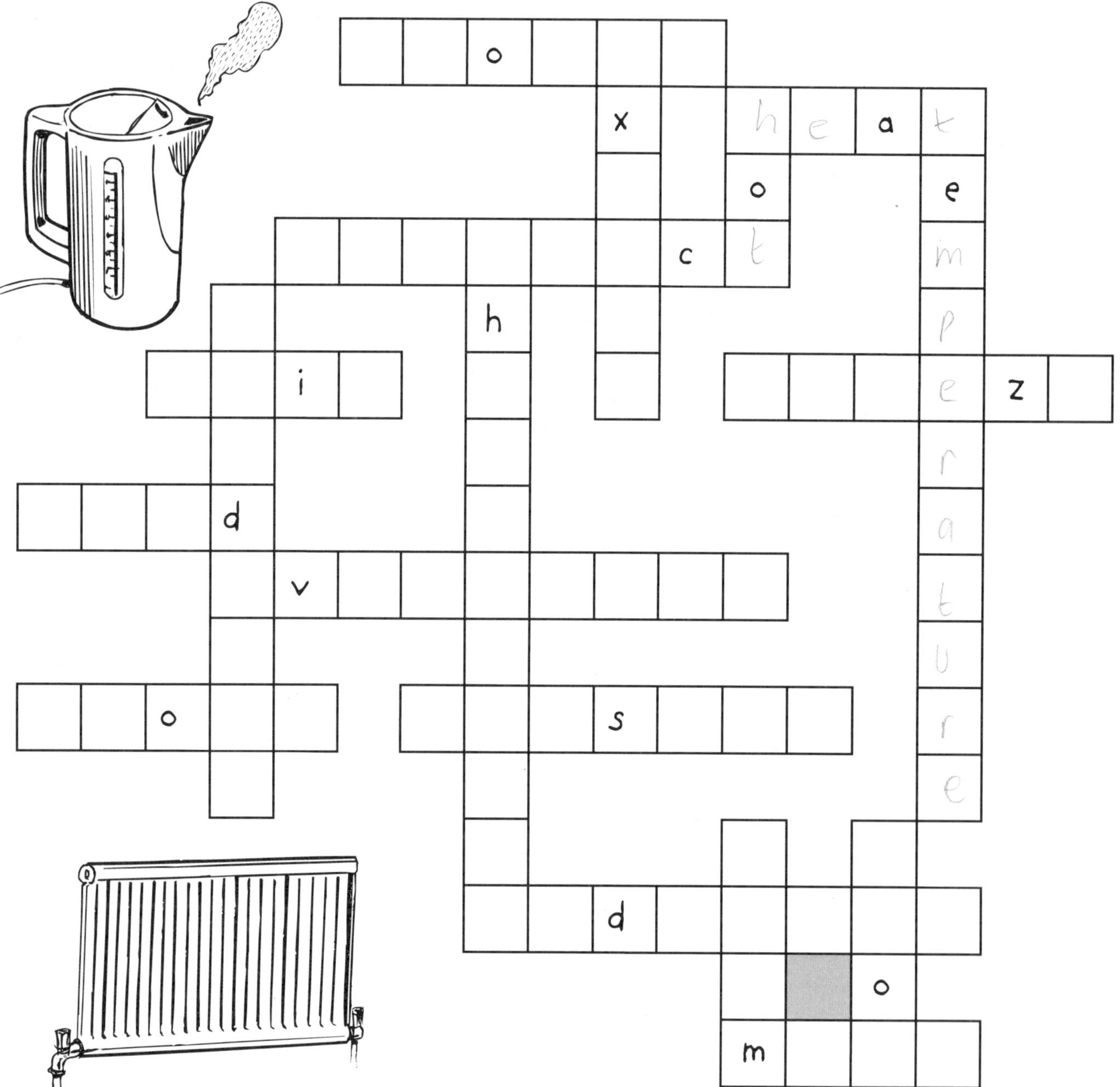

If you have time, write a definition for each word on another sheet of paper.

Expansion and contraction

Read the ten sentences below. The words in capital letters are in the wrong sentences. Sort them out and write the correct word in the box for each sentence. The first one has been done for you.

1. Materials **FREEZES** when they are heated.

1. EXPAND

2. Materials **HEATED** when they are cooled.

2.

3. Heated **THERMOMETERS** expand much more than either liquids or solids.

3.

4. ~~**EXPAND**~~ liquids expand much more than solids.

4.

5. Heated **GASES** expand much less than either liquids or gases.

5.

6. **IRON** air can burst a balloon if the balloon goes near a fire.

6.

7. When water **GAPS** it expands.

7.

8. **SOLIDS** are left between railway lines, and between sections of concrete road to allow for expansion.

8.

9. Liquids that expand rapidly, such as alcohol and mercury, are used in **CONTRACT**.

9.

10. Metals such as **EXPANDING** and steel expand or contract more than most other solids.

10.

COVER THESE INSTRUCTIONS WHEN PHOTOCOPYING.

Notes for the teacher

Ideally, before working on this sheet, the children should have been given some background information and carried out practical investigations into the relative expansion and contraction rates of solids, liquids and gases.

Changing temperatures

Imagine you have just returned home from an early spring holiday in a cottage in the Lake District. The weather was varied, but the scenery was magnificent! You took some photographs of the scenes.

On another sheet of paper, write a letter to your pen-friend in France, explaining where you went and what you did. In your letter, include eight words from the word bank at the bottom of the page. Use each word in a different sentence. Look carefully at the pictures when you are choosing words from the word bank.

freezing temperature warm cool
boiling hottest coldest melting frost
heating snow thermometer

Test it

Mrs Twigg's class use the Internet to send e-mails to a school in Australia. They often exchange experiments and discuss the things they have found out. Josh has just received this message from his friend Kieran in Australia.

From: Kieran Holmes <k.holmes@asps.edu.au> Page 1 of 1
To: Josh Allen <josh@joshallen.ftnet.co.uk>
Date: 19 April 2002 10:06
Subject: Amazing Puddle Experiment!

Hi Josh,
We did an **experiment** yesterday to look at **evaporation**. We'd been waiting ages to do it, because it hadn't rained and we needed some puddles in the school playground. You shouldn't have to wait long to do the experiment in your school, because from what I hear it rains a lot where you live!
Rain had fallen heavily during the night, and by the following morning there were many puddles in the playground. The morning was sunny. Our teacher, Mr Ford, took us outside at 9 o'clock and asked us to **measure** the **approximate** width of one of the puddles. The puddle I chose measured about 30cm in width.
We spent the morning going out and measuring the puddles at hourly intervals, then **recording** our results on a diagram. I have attached a copy of the diagram (attachment 1). We discovered that during the period of our **measurements** the puddles became much smaller. Our teacher told us that virtually none of the water in the puddles was **soaking** into the playground. So where had the water gone?
Mr Ford explained that the water had **evaporated**. This meant that it had changed from a liquid into a gas. This gas was called **water vapour**. Mr Ford told us that the higher the **temperature** of the water, the more quickly the water **evaporates**. The morning had been quite warm and sunny, so the size of the puddles had decreased rapidly over the three hours of our measurements.
When we had finished taking our measurements, we recorded our results on a **graph**. I've included a copy of the graph for you to look at (attachment 2).
Ask Mrs Twigg whether you can do the same experiment in your class. Then we can **compare** results and discuss the reasons for any differences.
Bye for now,
Kieran.

attachment 1

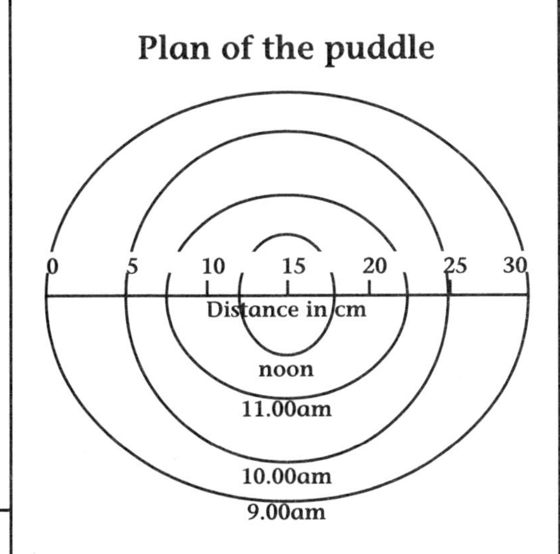

attachment 2

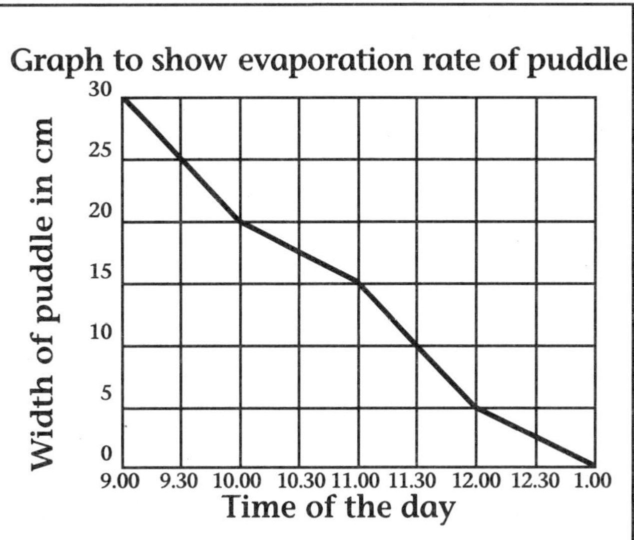

Test it

1. Yesterday, Kieran did an **experiment** at school. What was the **experiment** looking at?

____

2. Why had Kieran and his friends had to wait so long to carry out their **experiment**?

____

____

3. What was the first thing Kieran's teacher asked the children to do when they were taken outside?

____

____

4. What was the main thing the children discovered during the three hours of their **measurements**?

____

5. The water in the puddles was **evaporating**. What is happening to water when it **evaporates**?

____

____

6. Approximately how wide was the puddle at:

a) 10.00am? ______________ **b)** noon? ______________

7. At what time do you think the puddle was **approximately**:

a) 15cm wide? ______________ **b)** 25cm wide? ______________

8. What had happened to the puddle by 1.00pm? ______________

9. Draw a ring on the diagram below to show the **approximate** size of the puddle at 10.30am.

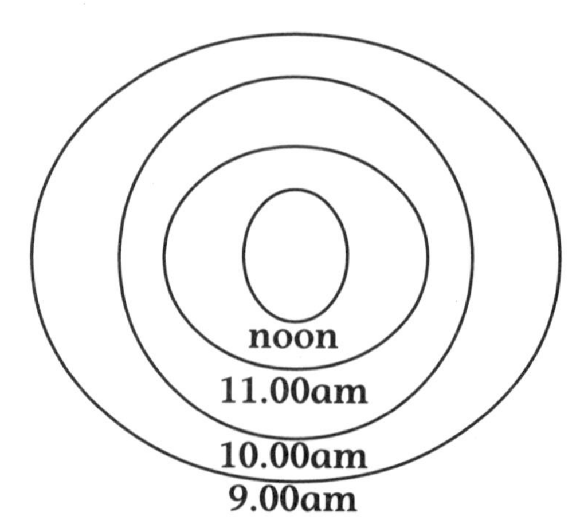

Describe how the result of the **experiment** would have been different if it had been carried out on:

a) a warmer day

b) a cooler day.

Include puddle diagrams and/or graphs with your written predictions.

Test it

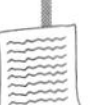

1. Underline the word that describes what Kieran's **experiment** was designed to look at.

condensation   evaporation   melting   disappearing

2. What had Kieran's teacher been waiting for before they could carry out the **experiment**? ____________

3. Cross out the incorrect words in these sentences.

a) As the day went by, Kieran and his friends discovered that the puddles became much **smaller / larger** in size.

b) Kieran's teacher told the children that virtually **all / none** of the water in the puddles was soaking into the playground.

4. Complete this sentence.

When water **evaporates** it changes from a __________ into a __________ .

5. At what times did Kieran **measure** the width of the puddle? Write the times in the boxes.

6. Look at the **graph** in attachment 2. Write the **approximate** width of the puddle at:

a) 9.30am ________ **b)** 10.00am ________ **c)** 11.00am ________

d) 11.30am ________ **e)** noon ________ **f)** 12.30pm ________

7. How many hours did it take for the puddle to dry up? ____________

8. Draw a ring on this diagram to show the **approximate** size of the puddle at 10.30am.

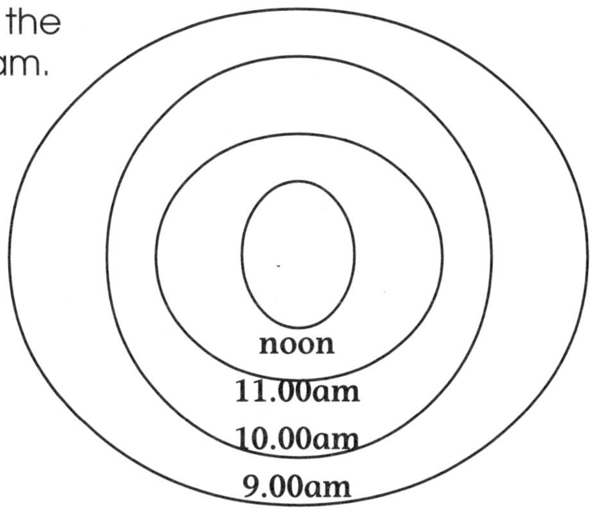

Discuss and then write about how the result of the **experiment** would have been different if it had been carried out on:

a) a warmer day

b) a cooler day.

Keeping in heat

Do this **experiment** on your own or with a friend. You are going to find out whether cotton wool is useful for keeping in heat.

thermometer

You will need: a copy of the 'Report sheet', two jam jars of equal size (labelled A and B), two laboratory thermometers, two rubber bands, cotton wool, a container with enough warm water (at approximately 60°C) to fill both jam jars.

cotton wool

warm water

What to do:

- Wrap a thick layer of cotton wool around the outside surface of Jar A. Secure the cotton wool using the two rubber bands.
- Pour equal amounts of warm water into the two jars.
- Place a thermometer in each jar. Check that the temperature of the water in both jars is the same.
- Measure the temperature every five minutes for half an hour. Record the readings on the chart below.
- Transfer the information on the chart to the graph. Plot the coordinates for Jar A first, marking them neatly with small red crosses. Try to draw a smooth red curve through the points. Now do the same for Jar B, using blue for the crosses and curve.
- Fill in the 'Report sheet'.

Time in minutes	Temperature in °C	
	Jar A	Jar B
0	60	60
5		
10		
15		
20		
25		
30		

Graph to show how the water cooled in Jar A (red) and Jar B (blue)

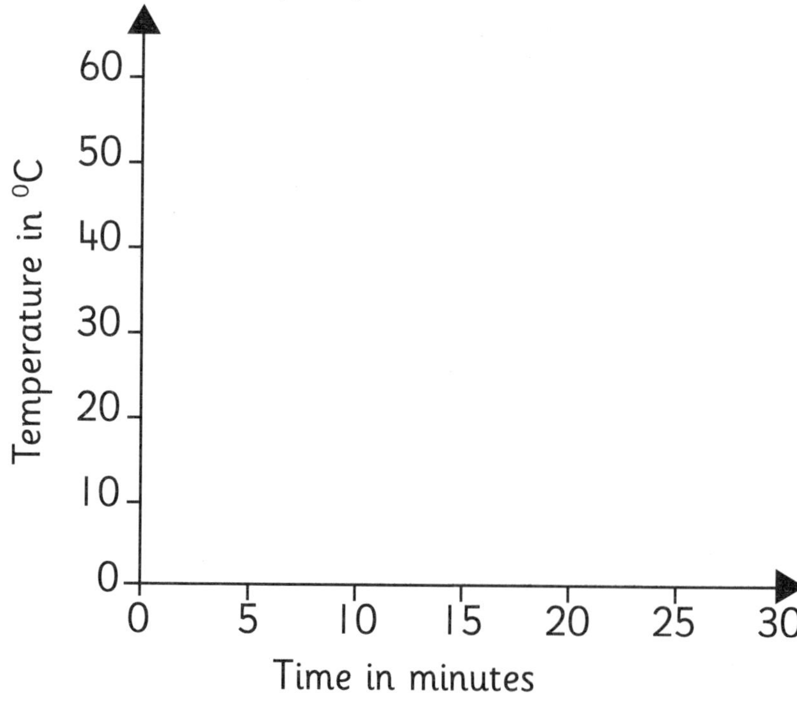

Report sheet

2

Write a report on your **experiment** or **investigation**.
Include **drawings** or labelled **diagrams** if possible.

Investigation title:

Purpose of the investigation:

The equipment I (we) used:

What I (we) did:

What I (we) found out:

Material properties

Vicky and Asim **investigated** the materials some things had been made from.

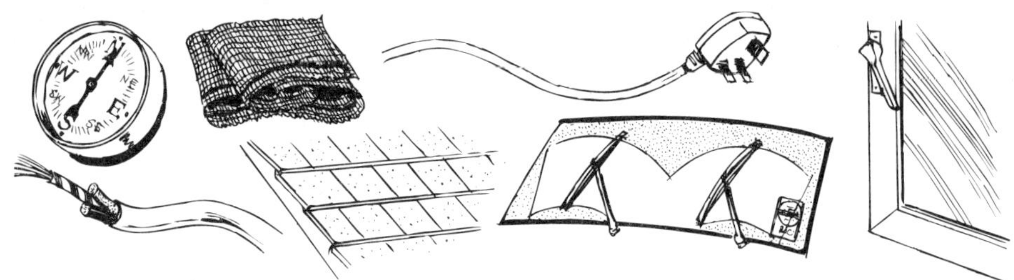

Complete each sentence below by choosing the correct ending from the box. Choose the endings for all the sentences before you start to write.

electrical conductor	transparent	electrical insulator
flexible magnetic	waterproof	absorbent

1. The needle in a compass is made of **steel** because steel is ______________________.

2. Glass is used for windows because it is ______________________.

3. A dishcloth is made of **cotton** because cotton is ______________________.

4. Plastic is used on the outside of electrical cables because it is an ______________ ______________.

5. Rubber is used for windscreen wiper blades because it is ______________.

6. Slate is used for roofs because it is ______________.

7. Copper is used for electrical wiring because it is an ______________ ______________.

Amarla looked at some other materials. She started to record the properties of each material in a table. Complete the table for her.

Materials	Properties				
	waterproof	flexible	absorbent	transparent	magnetic
newspaper	no	yes	yes	no	no
aluminium					
iron					
wax					
clear plastic					

Water and the water cycle

All living things depend on water for their survival. As well as the part it plays in essential life processes, water is also used by people for:

- recreation
- transport
- industrial processes
- electricity generation
- sanitation.

Most of the water on Earth has been here as long as the Earth itself. The water is continually being recycled over long periods of time in a **process** called the **water cycle**. The water cycle works in the following way.

1. When water is warmed by the Sun, it **evaporates** into the **atmosphere** in the form of a **gas** called **water vapour**. A huge amount of water evaporates from oceans, seas and lakes every day. The atmosphere also receives water vapour from animals when they **exhale** and from plants when they **transpire**.

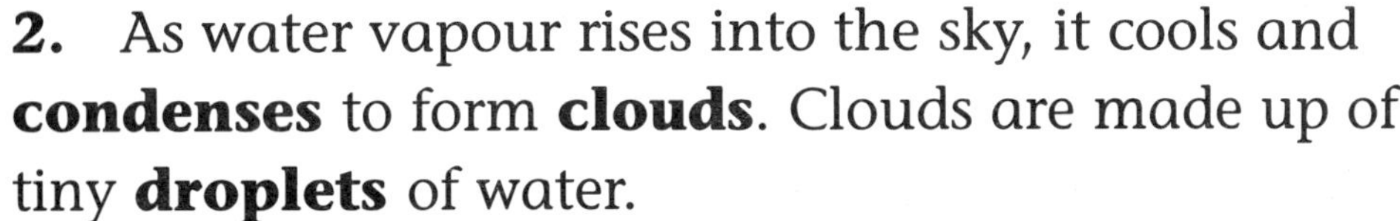

2. As water vapour rises into the sky, it cools and **condenses** to form **clouds**. Clouds are made up of tiny **droplets** of water.

3. The clouds are blown by the wind over the land.

4. When clouds rise over higher ground, larger drops of water form and start to fall as **rain**. If it is very cold, the water will **freeze** and fall as **hail**, **snow** or **sleet**. Rain, hail, snow and sleet are all different forms of **precipitation**.

5. The rain collects in streams and rivers and flows back to the sea, and the whole process starts again.

Some rainwater also **soaks** into the ground. Some of this water is taken in by plants through their roots, and is released through their leaves as water vapour when the plants transpire.

Water and the water cycle

1. What is the **process** called that is continually recycling the Earth's water supply? ____________________

What causes water to **evaporate** from oceans, seas and lakes into the **atmosphere**? ____________________

What are **clouds** made of? ____________________

2. Name three forms of water that fall from **clouds**.

________________ ________________ ________________

3. What is the general name for all forms of water falling from **clouds**? ____________________

4. True or false? Circle the correct answer.

a) Some rainwater is taken in by plants through their leaves. **True / False**

b) The roots of plants give off water vapour to the atmosphere. **True / False**

5. Complete this sentence, using the words in the box below.

When ____________ rise over higher ____________, large ____________ of ____________ form and start to fall as ____________.

ground	rain	clouds	drops	water

6. What do you think happens to water that **soaks** into the ground and is not taken up by plant roots?

____

____

7. Which word in the text means 'the air around the Earth'? ____________________

8. Write these words and their meanings on another sheet of paper.

a) **exhale** b) **transpire**

Draw and label a diagram to show how water gets from the ocean to the land and back again. Discuss with your friends what your diagram shows. Ask your teacher if you can display your work.

Water and the water cycle

1. Complete these sentences.

a) The water on Earth is continually being recycled in a ______________

called the ______________ ______________.

b) The heat of the Sun causes water to ______________ into the

______________ from oceans, seas and lakes.

c) As **water vapour** rises into the sky, it cools and ______________ to form

______________.

d) **Clouds** are made up of tiny ______________ of water.

2. Which of these words are forms of water? Tick the correct boxes.

sleet	☐	liquid	☐	cycle	☐	hail	☐
gas	☐	snow	☐	rain	☐	soak	☐

3. Plants take in water through their roots. Through which part of a plant does water escape into the air as **water vapour**?

____

4. What does most rainwater flow into to get back to the sea?

____

5. What do you think happens to water that **soaks** into the ground and is not taken up by plant roots?

____

____

6. Write the correct label in the empty box on the diagram. Choose from the three words given below.

cloud droplet atmosphere

Earth

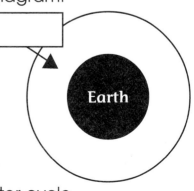

7. Write these words and their meanings on another sheet of paper.

a) **evaporate** **b)** **condense**

Ask your teacher for copies of pages 48 and 49. Follow the instructions to label the diagram of the water cycle.

Water cycle

You will need: the 'Water cycle 2' sheet, scissors, glue.

What to do: Cut out these labels and paste them in their correct places on the diagram of the **water cycle**.

When **clouds** rise over higher ground, large drops of water form and start to fall as **rain**.

The **rain** collects in streams and rivers and flows back to lakes and the sea.

Rain falls into the sea.

The **rain** collects in streams and rivers and flows back to lakes and the sea.

Water **evaporates** into the **atmosphere** from the surface of lakes.

The **clouds** are blown by the wind over the land.

Water **evaporates** into the **atmosphere** from the surface of the sea.

Animals breathe out **water vapour** when they **exhale**.

Plant leaves give off **water vapour** into the **atmosphere** when they **transpire**.

As **water vapour** rises into the sky it cools and **condenses** to form **clouds**.

COVER THESE INSTRUCTIONS WHEN PHOTOCOPYING.

Notes for the teacher

This sheet and 'Water cycle 2' can be used at any time, or in conjunction with the extension task on page 47. Children might find the labelled diagram of the water cycle on page 81 of *Developing Science Language for Materials and their properties with 8–9 year olds* useful for reference purposes when using this sheet.

2

Water cycle

Paste the labels you have cut out from 'Water cycle 1' in the correct places on this diagram of the **water cycle**.
A glue symbol ( ) on the diagram shows you where a label should be pasted.
When you have finished, ask your teacher if you can display your work.

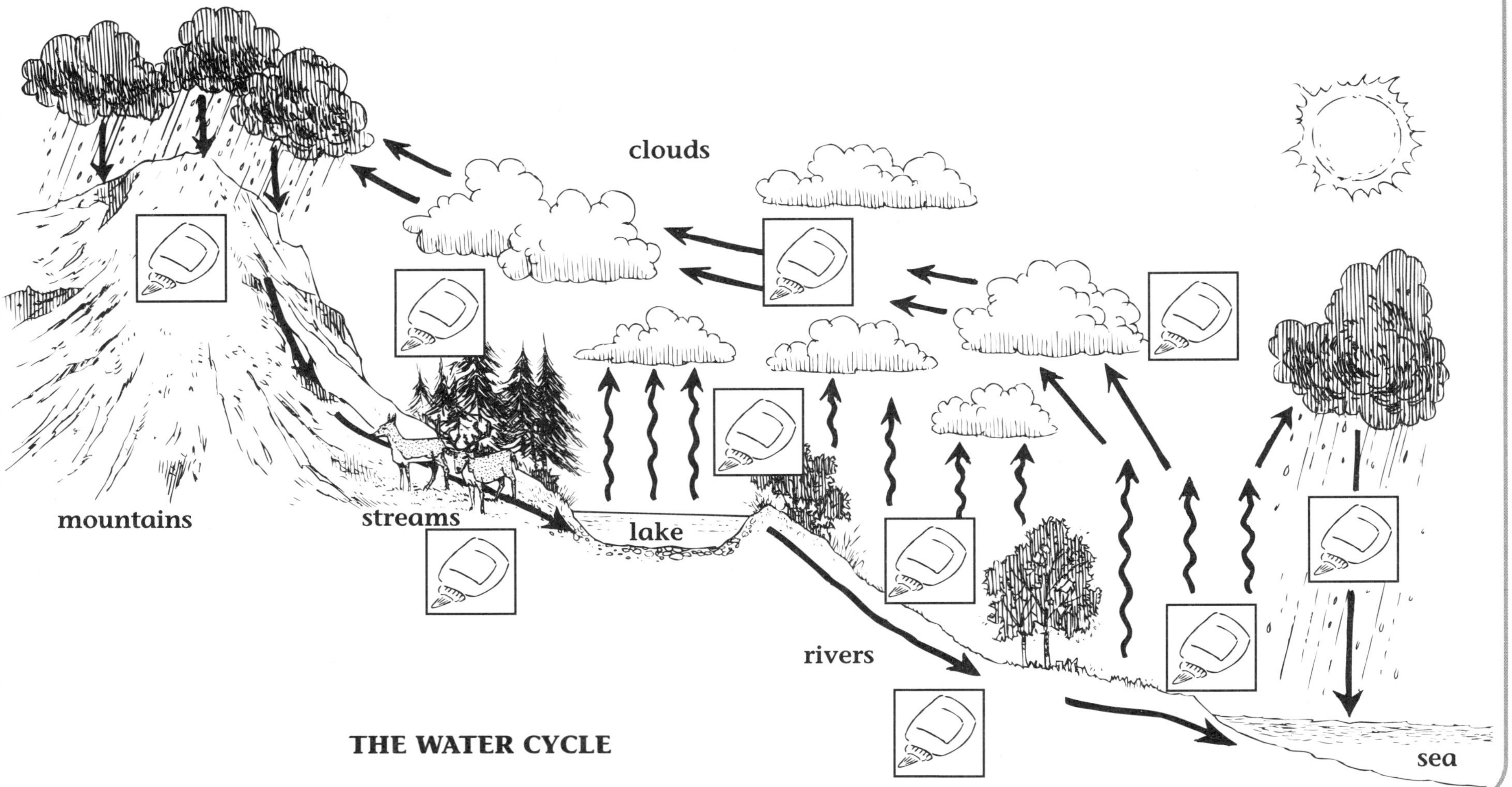

COVER THESE INSTRUCTIONS WHEN PHOTOCOPYING.

Notes for the teacher
This sheet and 'Water cycle 1' can be used at any time, or in conjunction with the extension task on page 47. Enlarge this page to A3 size before use.

Evaporation and condensation

Read the text below. Each missing word is marked by a letter. The words you need are in the grid on the left. In the grid on the right, write the number of each word next to the letter that represents it. The first one has been done for you.
Organise all the words on a blank sheet of paper before you fill in the grids.

Evaporation and condensation

Water is changing into water vapour all the time. When this happens, we say the water is evaporating. The **A** the water is, the more quickly it **B**. When water is **C**, it is **D** as quickly as it can. Water evaporates from the surfaces of oceans, **E** and lakes. Some water also evaporates from the surface of living animals when they **F** and the leaves of living plants when they **G**. Some water evaporates from dead things. When water evaporates from dead things, they **H** up. Water evaporating from any **J** leaves the rest of the mixture behind. **K**, for instance, is left when sea-water evaporates from a rock pool. Dried mud remains when water evaporates from a **L** puddle. When air becomes **M** enough, some of the water vapour it contains changes into tiny **N** of water. When this happens, we say the water vapour is **P**. The warmer the **Q** is, the more water vapour it can hold. If **R** air touches a cold surface, droplets of water form on the surface. This happens on the outside of a glass tumbler if the tumbler contains an ice-cold drink. **S** on grass and other outdoor plants in the early **T** is caused by **U** vapour condensing on a surface that is **V** than the air.

1 dew
2 colder
3 water
4 evaporates
5 air
6 dry
7 morning
8 seas
9 transpire
10 condensing
11 mixture
12 muddy
13 ~~warmer~~
14 evaporating
15 cold
16 warm
17 boiling
18 droplets
19 salt
20 perspire

A	13
B	
C	
D	
E	
F	
G	

H	
J	
K	
L	
M	
N	
P	

Q	
R	
S	
T	
U	
V	

Formation of rocks and soils

The **crust** of the Earth is made from many different kinds of rock. The different types vary greatly in **appearance**, **texture** and **permeability**.

The appearance and texture of rocks, and whether or not they let water pass through them, are mainly the result of the way they have been formed.

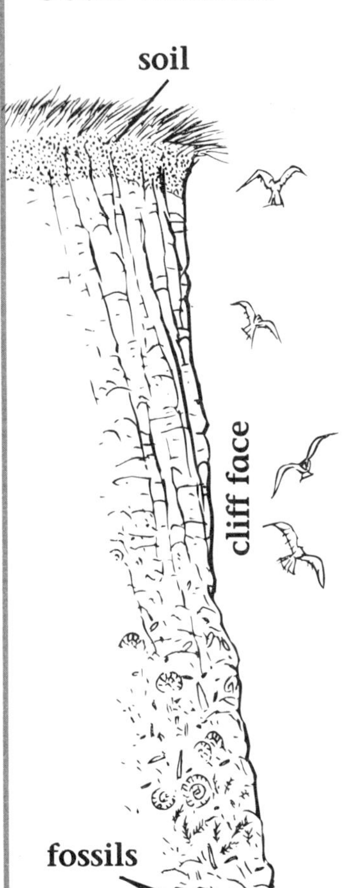

- Some rocks are made in layers from small **particles** of rock and the remains of dead plants and animals. These are called **sedimentary** rocks. **Limestone** and **chalk** are examples of rocks made in this way. The dead plant and animal remains can often be seen as **fossils** in the rock.
- Other rocks are made from sedimentary rock that has been changed by heat. These are called **metamorphic** rocks. **Marble** and **slate** are examples of this kind of rock.
- Other rocks are formed when hot, liquid rock pushes itself upwards from deep inside the Earth and then cools. These are called **igneous** rocks. **Granite** and **quartz** are formed in this way.

All kinds of rock can occur in different sizes. We call different-sized pieces of rock by different names. Very small particles of rock are known as **sand**, larger pieces are called **grit**, **stones** and **pebbles**, and even larger pieces are called **boulders**.

clay, sand and gravel particles
humus
water
air space

Soil makes up the outer cover of the Earth's crust. It is a mixture of **clay**, **sand**, **gravel**, **humus** (decaying plant and animal matter), **air spaces** and **water**.

Formation of rocks and soils

1. What is the **crust** of the Earth made from? Answer with a full sentence. ______

______

2. Which group of rocks is:

a) made in layers from other small **particles** of rock? ______

b) made from rock that has been changed by heat? ______

c) made from hot, liquid rock that pushes itself upwards from deep inside the Earth? ______

3. Name two kinds of rock that will probably contain **fossils**.

______ ______

4. Name three kinds of rock that are made in different ways.

______ ______ ______

5. Draw and label a diagram in this box to show a magnified view of a sample of **soil**.

6. Write the meaning of each word.

a) **appearance** ______

b) **texture** ______

c) **permeable** ______

7. Find a dictionary definition of '**fossil**' and write it here.

______

Some rocks are made by the cooling of hot, liquid rock that has pushed up from inside the Earth. Discuss this with your friends, then draw and label a **volcano** to show it happening.

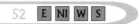

Formation of rocks and soils

1. Which part of the Earth is made from many different kinds of rock? ____________________

2. Tick the words that are the names of different groups of rock.

metamorphic	☐	ingenious	☐	igneous	☐
medallion	☐	sedimentary	☐	metallic	☐

3. Name one kind of rock that will probably contain **fossils**. ____________

4. Put each of these kinds of rock into the correct column on the chart.

granite marble
chalk quartz
limestone slate

Kind of rock		
sedimentary	**metamorphic**	**igneous**

5. Label this diagram of a magnified soil sample, using the words given in the box.

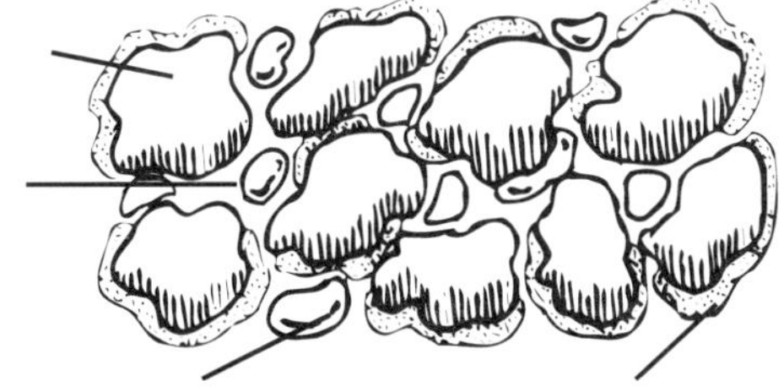

clay
sand
gravel
humus
air spaces
water

6. Draw a line to connect each word to its meaning.

appearance
texture
permeable

will allow water or air to pass through it
what something looks like
the way something feels when touched

7. 'The remains of a prehistoric animal or plant once buried in earth and now hardened like stone'.

What is this a definition of? ____________________

Some rocks are made by the cooling of hot, liquid rock that has pushed up from inside the Earth. Discuss this with your friends, then draw and label a **volcano** to show it happening.

Down to earth clues!

Work with a friend to solve the clues.
You will each need a copy of this sheet and a pencil.
Your teacher will explain what you have to do.

Set A clues

1. Goes hard when baked.

2. The group of rocks in which fossils are found.

3. Plants grow in this.

4. Rock made of sand.

5. Beach castles can be made from this.

6. Stone often carved and polished into statues.

7. Grass-covered ground.

8. Collection of very small stones.

9. Rock used as a roofing material.

10. Rocks changed by heat are called _ e _ a _ _ r p _ _ c.

Set B clues

1. Soft, white rock used for writing.

2. Collection of sharp, angular particles.

3. Small, rounded stone.

4. Decaying plant and animal remains.

5. The group of rocks formed from cooled lava.

6. Makes soil moist.

7. An igneous rock: _ r _ n _ t _.

8. Large, rounded stone.

9. Dead remains preserved in rock.

10. Whitish rock often having fossils.

Word list

pebble, sand, limestone, turf, sedimentary, slate, granite, chalk, water, grit, clay, soil, fossil, marble, sandstone, boulder, igneous, metamorphic, gravel, humus

Answers
1.
2.
3.
4.
5.

Answers
6.
7.
8.
9.
10.

COVER THESE INSTRUCTIONS WHEN PHOTOCOPYING.

Notes for the teacher

Agree which child will read out each set of clues. The child who reads the Set A clues must try to find the most suitable answers from the word list to the Set B clues. The child who reads the Set B clues must try to find the most suitable answers from the word list to the Set A clues. Each answer should be written carefully in the correct answer box.

Hard or soft?

In this **experiment** you are going to test different kinds of rock to find out how **hard** or **soft** each one is.
The **hardness** of a rock is measured on a scale of 1 to 10, with 1 being the **softest** and 10 the **hardest**. The scale is known as the Mohs scale of hardness. It is named after the German scientist Friedrich Mohs, who devised it over a century ago.

You will need: five different kinds of rock, including **granite** and **chalk**, a 10p coin, a steel nail and a steel file.

What to do:

- Scratch each rock in turn with your fingernail, a 10p coin, a steel nail and a steel file.
- Use the hardness scale to work out how hard each sample is. Write down the results on the chart. An example has been done for you.

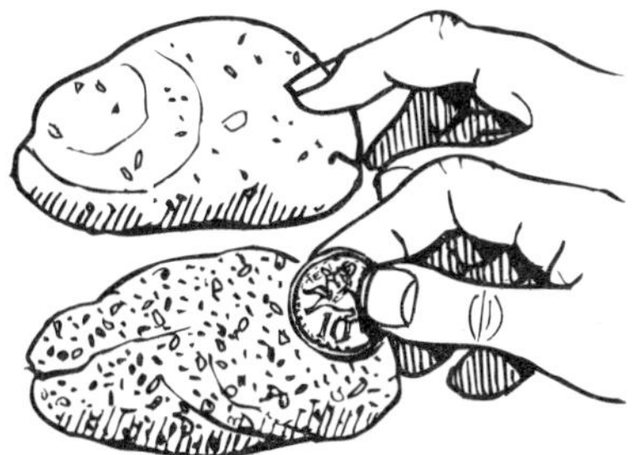

Hardness scale	Scratched with
1–2	fingernail
3	10p coin
4–5	steel nail
6–7	steel file

Rock	x = did not make a scratch 0 = made a scratch				Hardness scale
	Scratched with				
	fingernail	10p coin	steel nail	steel file	
sandstone	x	x	0	0	4–5

Write the names of the tested rocks in order of hardness, starting with the softest.

COVER THESE INSTRUCTIONS WHEN PHOTOCOPYING.

Notes for the teacher
Ask the children to bring a variety of small rock specimens into school. A basic rock set containing about 12 **named** rock specimens (available from most general educational suppliers) would be useful when the children are working on this sheet – unless you are an expert at identifying different rocks!

Inside the Earth

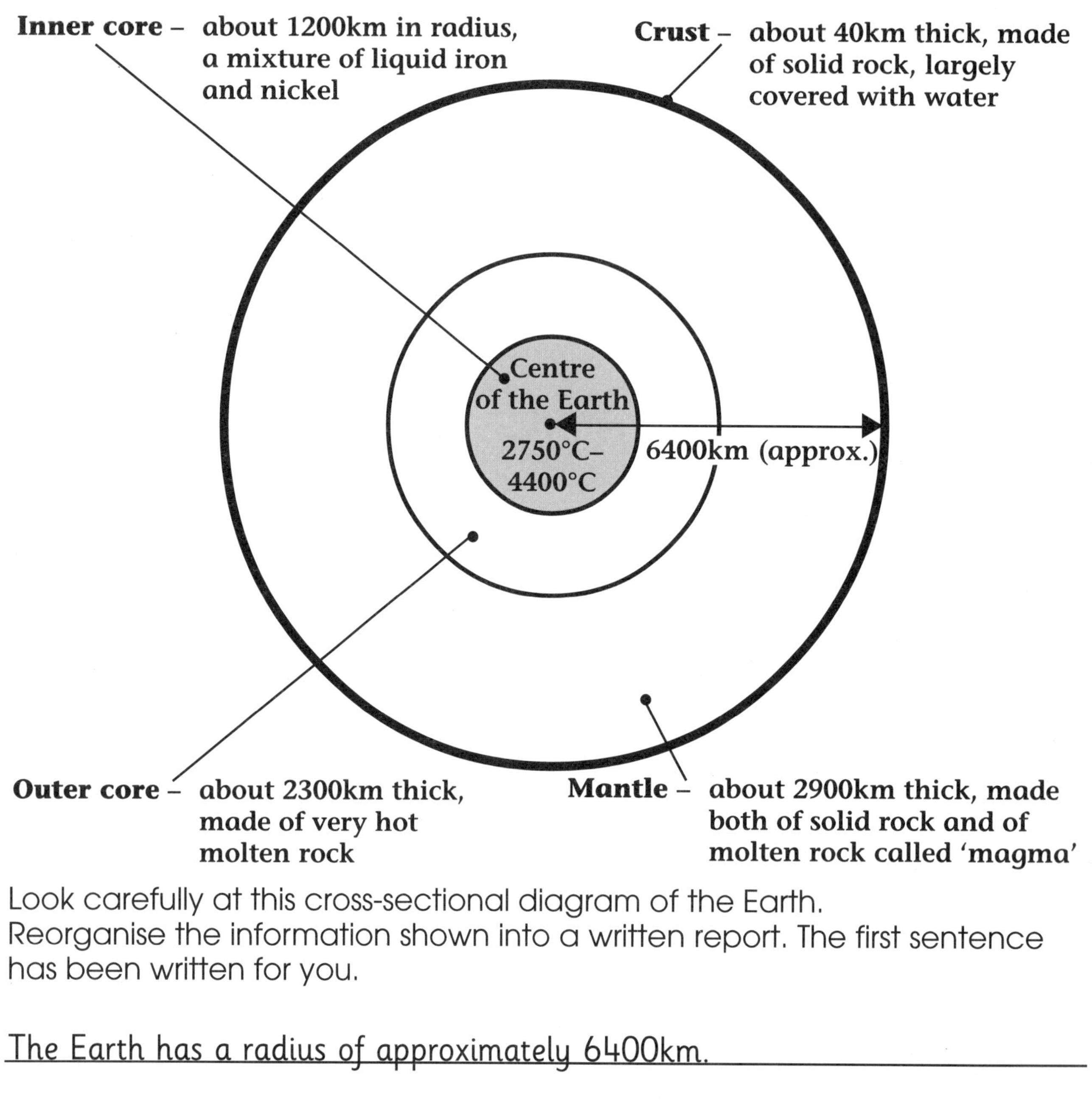

Look carefully at this cross-sectional diagram of the Earth. Reorganise the information shown into a written report. The first sentence has been written for you.

The Earth has a radius of approximately 6400km.

____

____

____

____

____

____

If you need more space, continue writing on the back of this sheet.

How rocks are formed

granite

limestone

slate

Read this information carefully, then carry out the tasks at the bottom of this page.

Rocks can be divided into three groups, according to the way in which they have been formed.

Igneous rocks

Heated molten rock (**magma**) forces its way through weak points in the Earth's **crust**. It cools down and **solidifies** either just beneath the Earth's surface or (following a **volcanic eruption**) at the surface. Rocks that form in this way, such as **basalt**, **quartz** and **granite**, are called **igneous** rocks. They have a **crystalline** structure.

Sedimentary rocks

Over long periods of time, rivers and waves break up rocks and wash them away. The rock particles are deposited as layers of **sediment** in shallow seas. These layers are squashed by the weight of the sediment and water above them to form solid rocks. Rocks that form in this way, such as **sandstone**, **limestone**, **chalk** and **clay**, are called **sedimentary** rocks.

Metamorphic rocks

Sometimes the appearance and hardness of sedimentary or igneous rocks are altered by heat and **pressure**, forming new rocks. Rocks formed in this way, such as **slate** and **marble**, are called **metamorphic** rocks. Slate was once clay, and marble was once limestone.

1. Select a specimen of granite, limestone and slate from a rock collection. Make a detailed drawing of each specimen in the appropriate box above. On another sheet of paper, describe the appearance of each rock.

2. On the same sheet of paper, create a table to display the information about the origin of rocks given in the passage. Think carefully about what headings you will need.

3. Underneath your table, write these words and their meanings.

magma solidify eruption sediment pressure

The rock cycle

Look carefully at this diagram of the **rock cycle**. Use it to help you answer the questions below.

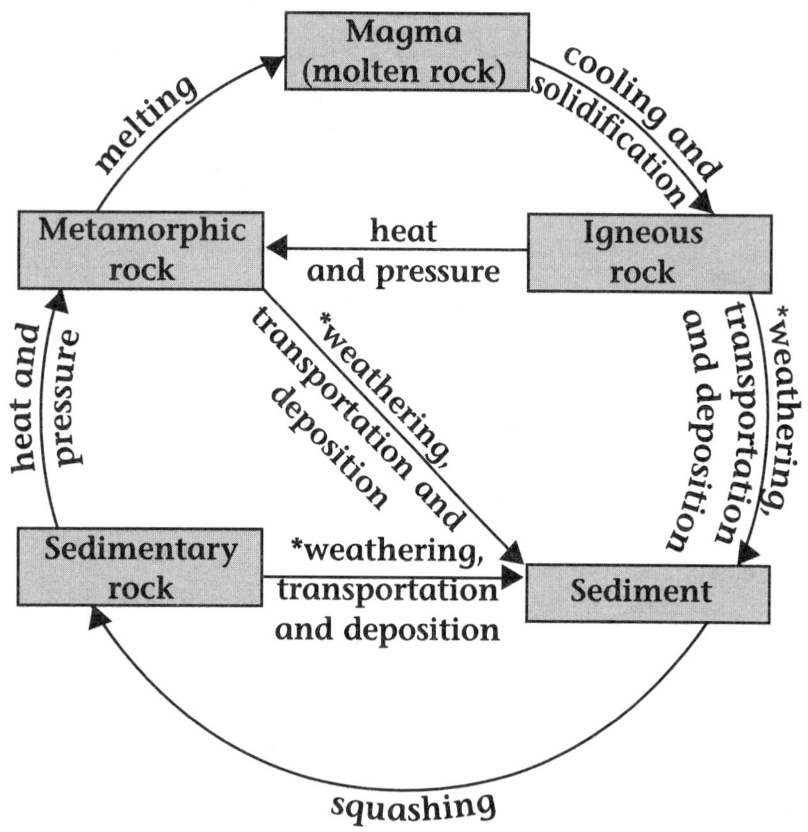

The rock cycle

***Weathering** is the breakdown of rocks into smaller **particles** by exposure to wind, rain, heating and cooling.

Transportation is the movement of the **particles** by means such as gravity, running water, glaciers, wind and waves.

Deposition is the laying down of the **particles** on the beds of lakes, seas and oceans.

1. When **magma** cools and solidifies, what type of rock is formed? ______________________

2. What kind of force acts on **sediment** to change it into **sedimentary** rock? ______________________

3. Complete this sentence.
Sedimentary rock can be changed into **metamorphic** rock by the action of

____

4. What three things have to happen to **metamorphic** rock for it to become **sediment** on the bed of a lake, sea or ocean?

______________ ______________ ______________

5. Describe what must happen to **magma** before it can become a **sedimentary** rock. Write your answer on a separate piece of paper.

Soil test

Some plants, such as heathers, grow best in **acid** soils. Others, such as wallflowers, grow better in **alkaline** or lime-based soils. You are going to test some soil types to find out how **acid** or **alkaline** they are.

A numerical scale known as the **pH scale** is used to measure **acidity** or **alkalinity**. It ranges in value from 0 to 14: where 0 is highly acidic, 7 is neutral and 14 is highly alkaline.

Coated paper strips called **universal indicator** strips change their colour according to the acidity or alkalinity of the substance they come into contact with. Each colour matches a number on the pH scale.

	strongly acidic			weakly acidic				neutral	weakly alkaline			strongly alkaline			
pH	**0**	**1**	**2**	**3**	**4**	**5**	**6**	**7**	**8**	**9**	**10**	**11**	**12**	**13**	**14**
indicator colour	red			orange		yellow		green	blue			violet			

You will need: five universal indicator strips, a tablespoon, a dropper, water and a sample of each of these soils: garden soil, peat, leaf-mould, growbag, field soil.

What to do:

- Add drops of water from a dropper to a level sample of the first soil in a tablespoon. Moisten the soil to a soft consistency.
- Press the coated side of a universal indicator strip firmly against the surface of the soil with your finger for one minute.
- Check the colour of the indicator strip against the scale on the diagram above. Record the result in the chart below.
- Carry out the same test with each of the other soil types. Remember to clean the spoon after each test.

Soil type	Indicator colour	pH value

Soil and its formation

The words in these boxes can all be used when writing about **soil**.
In each box, write what you would say about the word or phrase if you were asked to explain its meaning. The first one has been done for you.

weathering	sandy soil
Weathering is the decay and breakdown of the rocks of the Earth's crust by exposure to wind, rain, heating and cooling.	
humus	clay soil
bedrock	loam
climate	topsoil

On another sheet of paper, write a short essay on 'Soil and its formation'. Include some of the words and sentences from the boxes above.

Reversible and irreversible changes

Materials are constantly being changed. Some of these changes to materials can be undone. This means that the material can be changed back to how it was. These changes are called **reversible** changes.

Many reversible changes are caused by a change in **temperature,** which can alter the way a material looks and feels. A **rise** in temperature can make a solid change into a liquid, or a liquid change into a gas. A **fall** in temperature can make a gas change into a liquid or a liquid change into a solid. When a change like this happens, we say the material has undergone a **change of state**. The temperature at which these changes occur is different for different materials.

Ice, **water** and **water vapour** are examples of how a material can exist in three different **states** depending on the temperature.

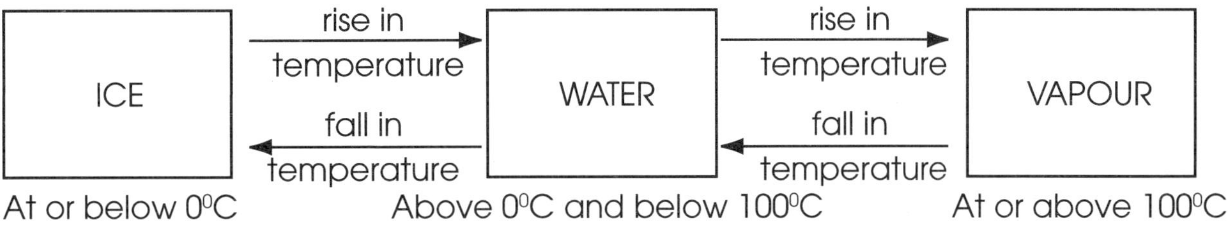

Changes of state happen through special **processes** such as **melting**, **freezing**, **evaporating**, **boiling** and **condensing**.

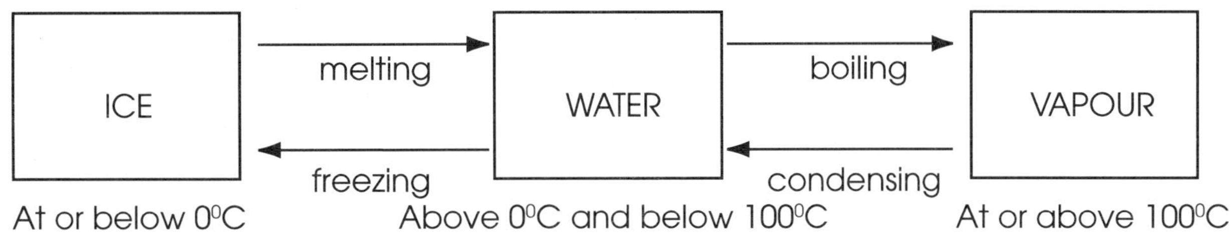

Some changes to materials cannot be undone. This means that the material cannot be changed back to how it was. New materials have been formed. These changes are called **irreversible** changes.

Irreversible changes include:

- **burning**
- **rusting**
- plaster of Paris setting when mixed with water
- a cake mixture cooking.

Reversible and irreversible changes

1. Answer these questions in complete sentences.

a) What type of change can be undone? ______________________

b) What type of change cannot be undone? ______________________

c) What are **ice**, **water** and **water vapour** examples of? ______________________

____

2. Swap two words in this sentence around and write the sentence correctly. Some changes to undone cannot be materials.

____

3. What can a **rise** in **temperature** do to:

a) a solid? ______________________

b) a liquid? ______________________

4. Tick the processes that involve a change of state.

boiling	☐	cycling	☐	freezing	☐	melting	☐
eating	☐	evaporating	☐	condensing	☐	snoring	☐

5. What do **burning** and **rusting** have in common?

____

6. Complete this flow chart diagram by adding words and arrows.

WATER → boiling → [ ] → [ ] → WATER → [ ] → [ ] → [ ] → WATER

7. Name four materials not mentioned in the text that will **melt** when left in bright sunlight.

____

____

____

____

Write and talk about four human activities that:

a) result in a material going through a **reversible** change

b) result in a material going through an **irreversible** change.

Reversible and irreversible changes

1. Write the missing word in each of these sentences.

a) ____________________ changes can be undone.

b) ____________________ changes cannot be undone.

c) **Ice**, **water** and water _______________ are examples of how a material can exist in three different **states**.

2. Choose two words from the box below and write them in the correct places in this sentence.

Some changes to _______________ cannot be _______________.

temperature	undone	materials	evaporating

3. Underline the correct word to use in each sentence.

a) A **rise** / **fall** in **temperature** can make a solid change into a liquid
b) A **rise** / **fall** in **temperature** can make a liquid change into a solid.

4. Tick the correct box to show what happens to **ice** when it **melts**.

it changes direction	☐	it changes state	☐
it changes speed	☐	it changes mass	☐

5. Name two types of **irreversible** change.

____________________ ____________________

6. Write the missing words in this flow chart.

VAPOUR → condensing → [ ] → freezing → [ ]
VAPOUR ← [ ] ← [ ] ← [ ] ← [ ]

7. Name three materials not mentioned in the text that will **melt** when left to stand in bright sunlight.

_______________ _______________ _______________

When a cake mixture is baked, an **irreversible** change takes place. Write and talk about other things people do that result in irreversible changes to materials.

A burning candle

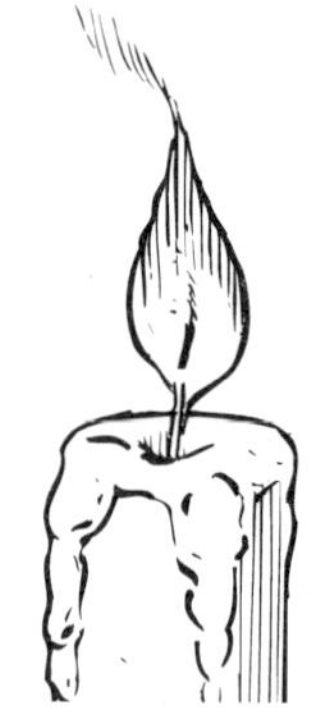

Darren and Georgia measured the **mass** of a candle on some scales. It had a mass of 20g. They placed the candle in a safe position in a sand tray, and their teacher lit it. Almost immediately a **liquid** appeared around the bottom of the **wick**.

What was the liquid and where had it come from?

Every half hour the children put out the candle and measured its mass. Then their teacher relit it. Their results are shown on this graph.

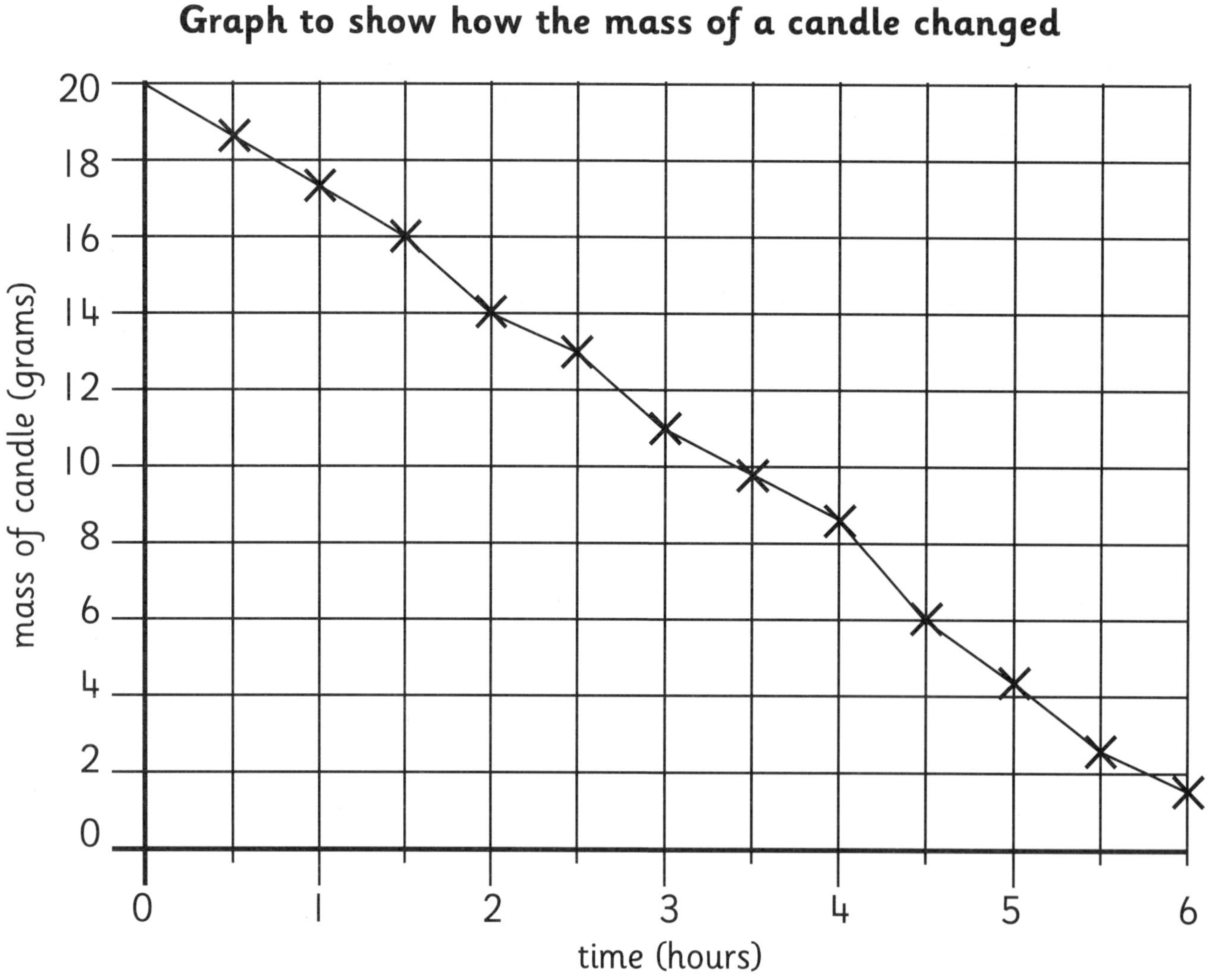

Graph to show how the mass of a candle changed

mass of candle (grams): 0, 2, 4, 6, 8, 10, 12, 14, 16, 18, 20

time (hours): 0, 1, 2, 3, 4, 5, 6

Answer these questions in complete sentences, on another sheet of paper.

1. What happened to the mass of the candle while it was burning?

2. What was the mass of the candle after it had been burning for two hours?

3. How much less than its starting mass was the mass of the candle after it had been burning for 270 minutes?

4. Is burning a candle a **reversible** change or an **irreversible** change?

Changing shape

This crossword contains 15 words, all related to different ways of changing shape. Write a suitable clue for each word. Use a dictionary to help you. One clue has been written for you.

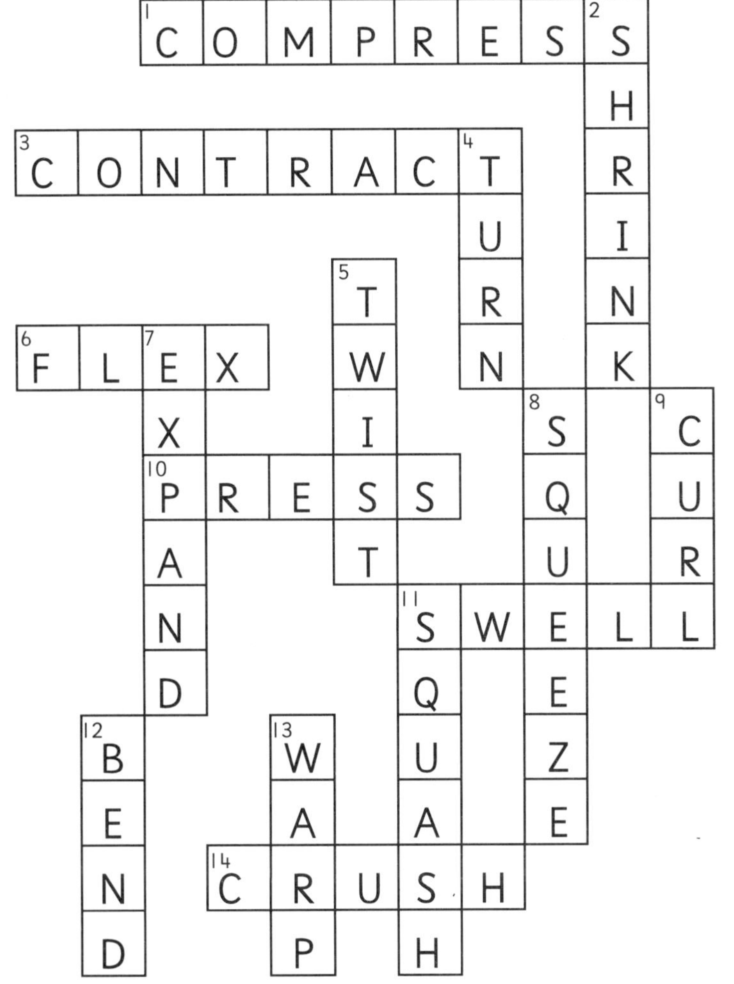

Across

1. ______________________

3. ______________________

6. ______________________

10. ______________________

11. ______________________

14. ______________________

Down

2. ______________________

4. ______________________

5. ______________________

7. ______________________

8. ______________________

9. ______________________

11. ______________________

12. To force something into a curve or angle.

13. ______________________

Reversible Snap

A game for 2 to 4 friends.

What to do:

- Shuffle the cards and deal them out to your friends. All players should start with the same number of cards.
- Take turns to put down a card. If two cards showing a **reversible** change occur together, any player can shout **'SNAP'**.
- The player who shouts **'SNAP'** collects all the cards – if you all agree that player was correct. He or she starts the next round.
- The winner is the player who ends up holding all the cards.

Water evaporating	Water evaporating	Water vapour condensing
Water evaporating	Water evaporating	Water vapour condensing
Water vapour condensing	Water boiling	Water boiling
Water vapour condensing	Water boiling	Water boiling
Chocolate melting	Ice melting	Water freezing
Chocolate melting	Ice melting	Water freezing

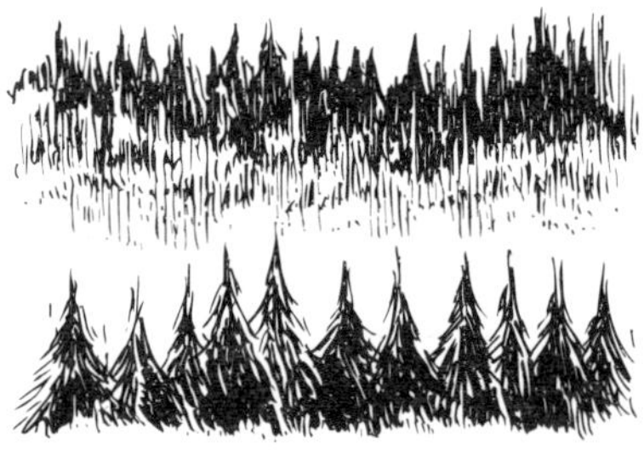

ENLARGE SHEETS TO A3 SIZE IF POSSIBLE.

Notes for the teacher:

To make this game, you need two copies of this page and two copies of 'Reversible Snap 2' on thin card, and scissors. Cut out the cards and give them to the children with a set of game instructions.

The focus of the game can be altered from reversible to irreversible changes if the children shout 'SNAP' when two cards showing an irreversible change occur together.

Reversible Snap

2

Water freezing

Water freezing

Sugar dissolving

Sugar dissolving

Salt dissolving

Salt dissolving

A candle burning

A candle burning

Natural gas burning

Natural gas burning

A match on fire

A match on fire

A nail rusting

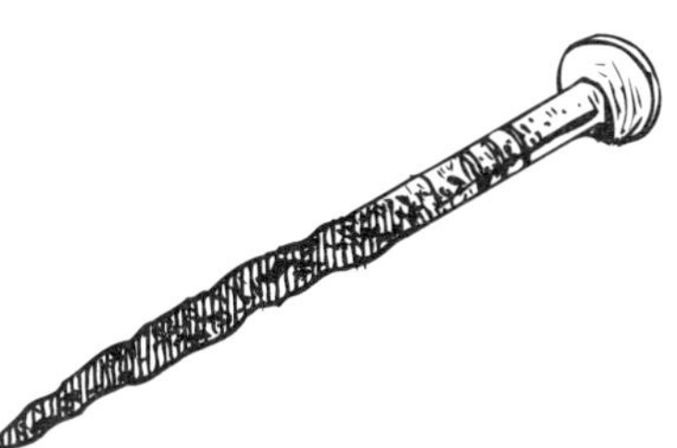

A nail rusting

A can rusting

A can rusting

Cakes cooking

Cakes cooking

An egg frying

An egg frying

'Firing' clay

'Firing' clay

Concrete hardening

Concrete hardening

Concrete hardening

Concrete hardening

Digesting food

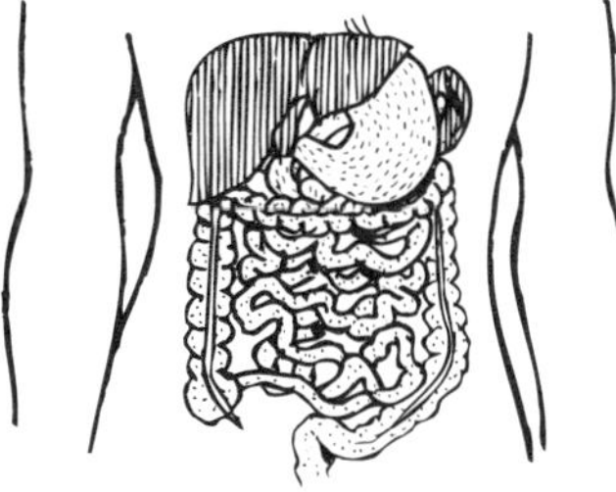

Digesting food

Toasting bread

Toasting bread

Fossil fuels round-the-class quiz

* Fossil fuels are non-...	ozone
Visible particles in the atmosphere when fossil fuels are burning.	renewable
Two types of oil used to power road vehicles.	smoke
A fossil fuel beginning with the letter **o**.	petrol and diesel
A worldwide threat caused by burning fossil fuels.	oil
Global warming is caused by the ___________ effect.	global warming
Coal, oil and gas are burned to make this type of energy.	greenhouse
A sulphurous gas produced mainly by burning coal.	electrical
Burning fossil _____ produces carbon dioxide and other gases.	sulphur dioxide
A fossil fuel beginning with the letter **c**.	fuels
The type of acid that can fall as rain.	coal
A place where fossil fuels are converted into usable energy.	sulphuric
The kind of rain that can kill trees and freshwater fish.	power station
Oil and natural ___ are both fossil fuels.	acid
The _____ layer filters out some of the harmful radiation from the Sun.	gas

COVER THESE INSTRUCTIONS WHEN PHOTOCOPYING.

Notes for the teacher:
Photocopy this sheet onto card. Cut along the solid lines. Fold each card in half along the dotted line, with the text on the outside. Fasten each card with tape or glue. If you are working with a small group, give each child a card. If you are working with the whole class, share the cards out one between two or three. All the cards must be given out.

The child (or group) with the card marked * reads the question aloud. The child with the answer to that question reads out the answer, then reads out the question on the back of the card. This goes on until the first child has read out the answer on his or her card.

Soluble or insoluble?

Look at the instructions on this workcard. They tell you what to do to find out whether a material will **dissolve** in water.

DISSOLVING

You will need: a teaspoon, a clear plastic container (about the size of a jam jar), water and a selection of materials (such as sand, salt, sugar, coffee, soil, crushed chalk, talcum powder, pencil shavings, flour and iron filings).

What to do:

- Half fill the container with clean water.
- Put a spoonful of sand into the water. Stir well for 30 seconds.
- Leave the **mixture** to stand for one minute. Then examine what it looks like.

*When certain materials are mixed with a liquid, they break up into tiny **particles** that are too small to be seen. When this happens, it means that the material is **soluble**. It has **dissolved** in the liquid to form a **solution**. In a solution, the dissolved material is called the **solute** and the liquid in which it is dissolved is called the **solvent**. When a material will not dissolve in the liquid it is placed in, it is said to be **insoluble**.*

- Write your result on the chart below by filling in the name of the material tested, then putting a tick in the correct column.
- Carry out the same test with all the other materials. Record your results.

material	soluble	insoluble	material	soluble	insoluble

25

CARD 3 ACTIVITY 6C

COVER THESE INSTRUCTIONS WHEN PHOTOCOPYING.

Notes for the teacher:
This sheet can be used either as a text for the comprehension activities on pages 70 and 71 or as an investigation activity in its own right. If the sheet is used as an investigation activity, the report sheet on page 43 can be used to provide additional literacy input.

Soluble or insoluble?

1. What will you find out by following the instructions on the workcard? Write your answer as a complete sentence.

____

____

2. Name five of the materials the workcard suggests you test.

____

3. What is the scientific name for the **mixture** formed when a solid **dissolves** in a liquid? ______________

4. Explain what is meant by 'an **insoluble** material'.

____

____

5. Why would this container of water be unsuitable to use in the investigation?

____

____

____

____

____

6. Which of the materials listed in the text do you think will **dissolve** in water? ______________

7. Write a dictionary definition for each word.

a) **particle** ______________

b) **solute** ______________

c) **solvent** ______________

Talk about whether **soluble** materials **dissolve** more easily in hot water than in cold water. How do you know? Can you think of any situations where this happens? How could you test your ideas?

Soluble or insoluble?

1. Write the missing word in this sentence.

You can find out whether a material will ______________ in water by following the instructions on the workcard.

2. Tick the materials that the workcard suggests you test.

coffee	☐	concrete	☐	sand	☐	rice	☐
sugar	☐	flour	☐	seeds	☐	soil	☐

3. Write the three words in the box in their correct places in this sentence.

A ______________ material will ______________ in a liquid to

form a ______________.

dissolve	solution	soluble

4. Cross out the incorrect words in this sentence.

An **insoluble / unstable / soluble** material will not dissolve in the liquid into which it is placed.

5. The workcard tells you how much water should be in the container for this investigation. Mark where the water level should be on this diagram.

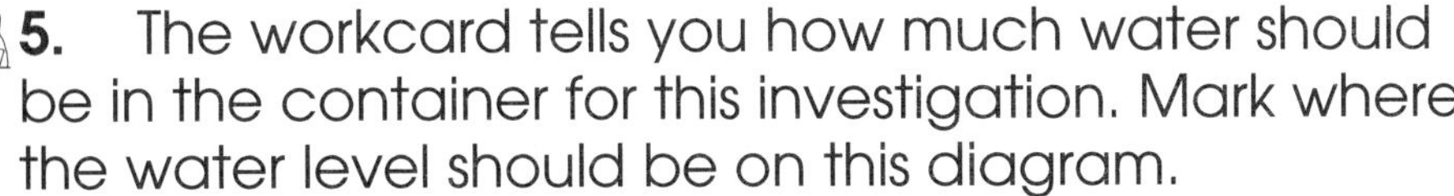

6. Circle the materials that you think will **dissolve** in water.

talcum powder   flour   salt   pencil shavings   sugar

7. Connect each word to its meaning.

particle		something that is dissolved in a liquid
solute		a liquid in which something is dissolved
solvent		a very small piece of something

Do you think sugar will **dissolve** faster in hot water than in cold water? Talk about this with some of your friends. How could you check whether you were right?

Definitions

Use a dictionary to help you with the words on this page.

1. Join each word to its meaning. One has been done for you.

mixture	can be dissolved
soluble	to change from water into water vapour
solvent	to be held up in air or in liquid
float	any liquid or gas that can flow easily
solute	to drop down through air or through liquid
fluid	liquid in which something is dissolved
evaporate	dissolved part of a solution
sink	two or more substances together

2. Write the word or the meaning in each empty box.

particle	
	to mix with a liquid to make a solution
liquid	
	cannot be dissolved
suspension	
	liquid containing a dissolved substance
substance	

Dissolving

1. Sarah and Ben have been finding out about materials.

They tested the materials listed below to find out which will **dissolve** in water. Tick the ones that you think will dissolve in water.

salt ☐ coffee ☐ flour ☐ sand ☐

clay ☐ chalk ☐ sugar ☐ sawdust ☐

How can Sarah and Ben **separate** a mixture of salt and clay?
To find out, read this passage and choose the right words from the box below to complete the sentences.

To separate a ______________ of salt and clay, the first thing the children should do is add ______________ to the mixture and ______________ for 30 seconds. They should then ______________ the mixture to remove the clay. Once the ______________ has been removed, they should heat the mixture to ______________ the liquid, leaving the salt behind.

sieve	water	evaporate	mixture	melt
clay	condense	stir	classify	filter

2. Tick the correct answer to each question.

a) What is the mixture called when a solid is dissolved in water?

a droplet ☐ a solution ☐ a suspension ☐ an alloy ☐

b) What is the dissolved material in a solution called?

the insulator ☐ the pollutant ☐ the solute ☐ the sequence ☐

c) What is a material called that cannot be dissolved?

insoluble ☐ irreversible ☐ porous ☐ reversible ☐

Temperature and solubility

Complete this sheet on your own or with a friend.

Mehmoud and Nasreen were asked to find out how much granulated sugar would **dissolve** in 100cm^3 of water at **room temperature**.

This table shows their results.

Spoonfuls of granulated sugar	Did it all dissolve in 100cm^3 of water?
2	yes
4	yes
6	yes
8	yes
10	no

Their teacher looked at the results and asked the children whether they thought the **solubility** of the sugar would increase if the temperature of the water was increased.

- Mehmoud said: 'If the temperature of the water is increased, it will make no difference to the solubility of the sugar.'
- Nasreen did not agree. She said: 'I think more sugar will dissolve if the temperature of the water is higher'.

In the space below, make planning notes for an **experiment** that will help you to decide which of the children was correct.

____

____

____

____

____

____

When your planning is complete, ask your teacher for a report sheet. Carry out the experiment and record your actual results.
Who was right, Mehmoud or Nasreen?

COVER THESE INSTRUCTIONS WHEN PHOTOCOPYING.

Notes for the teacher
The children will need a photocopy of the report sheet on page 43 when carrying out this activity.

Conductors and insulators

Thermal conductors and insulators

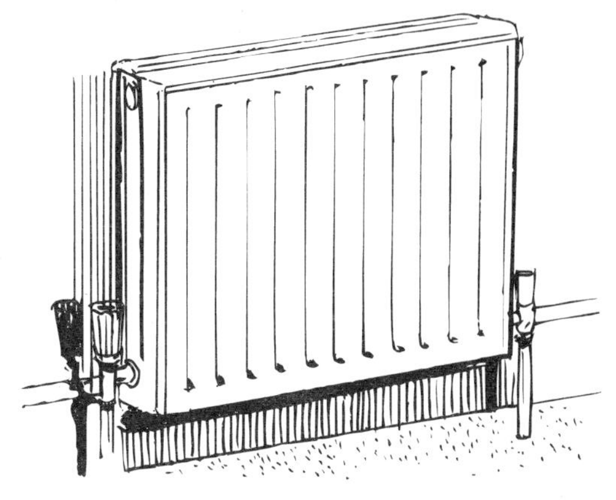

Materials that gain heat quickly and lose heat quickly are called **thermal conductors**. Materials that gain heat slowly and lose heat slowly are called **thermal insulators**. **Solids** are normally better thermal conductors than **liquids**. Most **metals**, especially **copper** and **aluminium**, are good thermal conductors, and that is why they are used in central heating systems for pipes and radiators.

Air is a good thermal insulator. Thermal insulating materials often contain many **air spaces**. The feathers on a bird and the hairs on a mammal have air spaces between them. This reduces heat loss from the body of the animal. Loose **snow** is a good thermal insulator because of the air spaces contained in it. **Wood** and **plastic**, though they do not contain many air spaces, are also good thermal insulators.

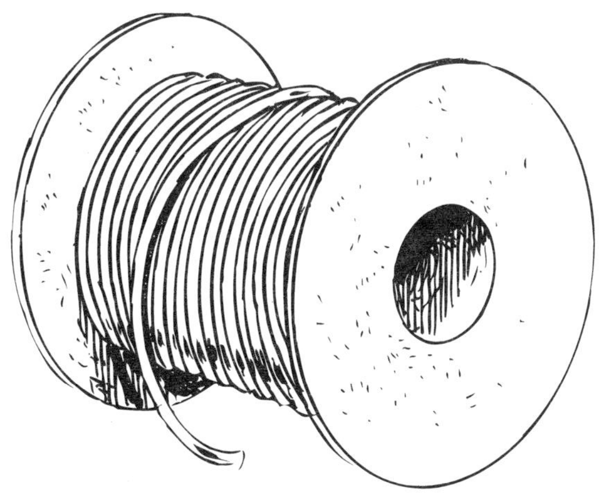

Electrical conductors and insulators

A material that allows electricity to flow through it is called an **electrical conductor**. A material that does not allow electricity to flow through it is called an **electrical insulator**. Most **metals** are good electrical conductors and will allow an electrical current to pass through them easily. That is why electrical wiring is made from metals such as **copper**, **brass** and **steel**.

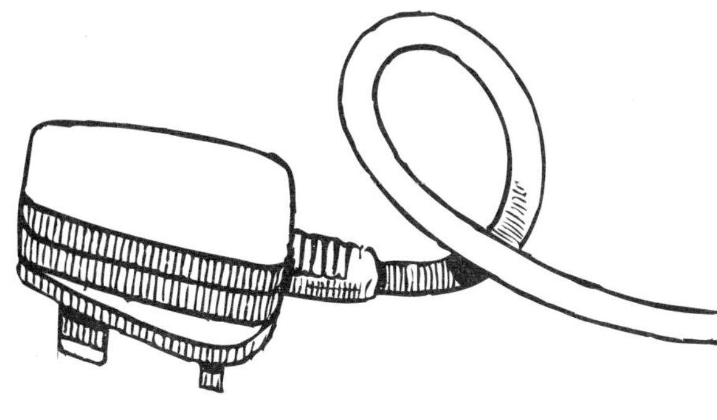

Glass, **rubber** and **plastic** are all good electrical insulators. Electrical current has great difficulty in passing through them. That is why electrical wires often have plastic surrounding them. The plastic covering protects people from getting an electric **shock** from the electricity flowing through the metal wire inside.

Conductors and insulators

1. What property does a **thermal conductor** have? ______________________

____

What property does a **thermal insulator** have? ______________________

____

2. Name two good **thermal conductors**. ____________ ____________

3. What do **thermal insulators** often contain? ______________________

4. Write a sentence that contains the words:

a) electrical conductor

____

b) electrical insulator

____

5. Why is electrical wiring made of such materials as **copper**, **brass** and **steel**?

____

6. Why do electrical wires often have an outer covering made of **plastic**?

____

7. Write the names of three suitable materials in each box.

thermal and electrical conductors	thermal and electrical insulators

8. Why do you think electric toasters have **thermally insulated** side panels?

____

____

9. Metal saucepans usually have **plastic** or **wooden** handles. Why is this?

____

Find out about the ways in which a house can be **thermally insulated** to stop heat escaping to the outside. Write what you find out on another sheet of paper.

Conductors and insulators

1. Write in the missing words in these sentences.

a) Materials that gain and lose heat quickly are called ______________________

______________________.

b) Materials that gain and lose heat slowly are called ______________________

______________________.

2. Tick the two materials that are good **thermal conductors**.

wood ☐ copper ☐ aluminium ☐ air ☐

3. Tick the two items listed here that do not contain many **air spaces**.

snow ☐ wood ☐ plastic ☐ feathers ☐ hair ☐

4. Cross out the incorrect word in this sentence.

A material that does not allow electricity to flow through it is called an electrical **fault / insulator / conductor**.

5. Write the names of three **metals** that can be made into electrical wiring.

______________________ ______________________ ______________________

6. Connect this sentence beginning to its most suitable ending.

The plastic outer covering on electrical wiring	stops people getting an electric **shock**.
	makes the wire look colourful.
	makes the wire smooth.

7. Write the name of each of these materials in the correct box.

steel rubber plastic copper wood aluminium

thermal and electrical conductors	thermal and electrical insulators

8. Name three types of clothes that you wear to stay warm on a cold day.

______________________ ______________________ ______________________

9. Most metal saucepans have **plastic** or **wooden** handles. Why is this?

____

Why is it important to make sure your house is well insulated? How can you do this? Write on another sheet of paper.

Electrical sort out

You will need: scissors, various materials of your own choice.

What to do:

1. Carefully cut around the picture of each object. Include the name of the material it is made from.

2. Decide on a way of presenting the pictures that will show other children and adults which of the objects in the pictures are good **electrical conductors** and which are good **electrical insulators**.

rubber	copper	gold	iron
aluminium	bronze	wood	plastic
steel	leather	water	brass
glass	polythene	silver	concrete

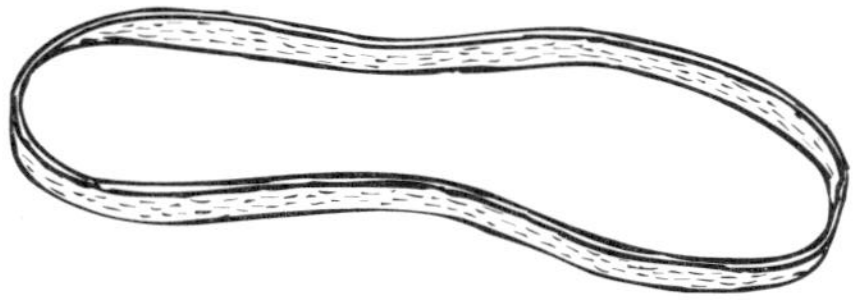

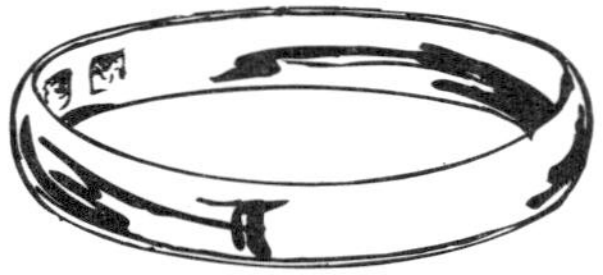

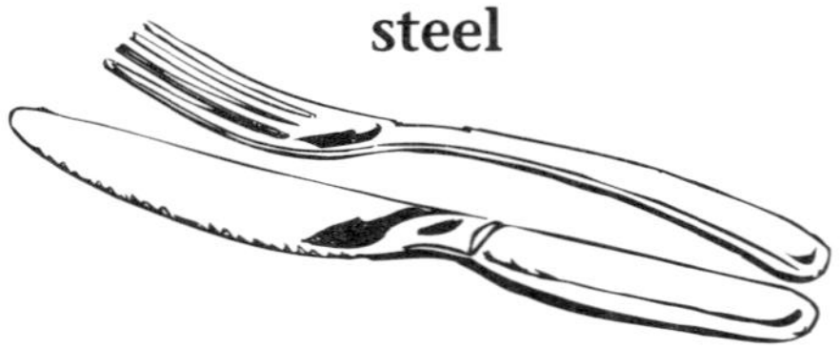

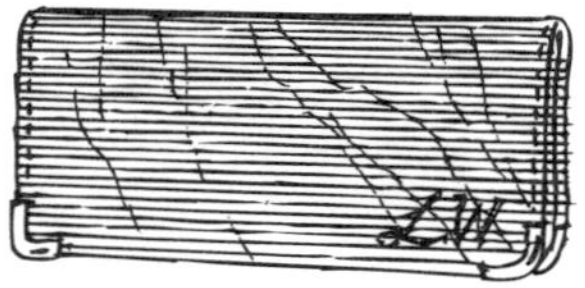

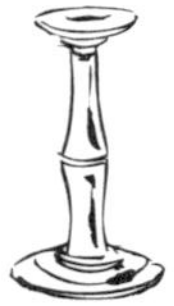

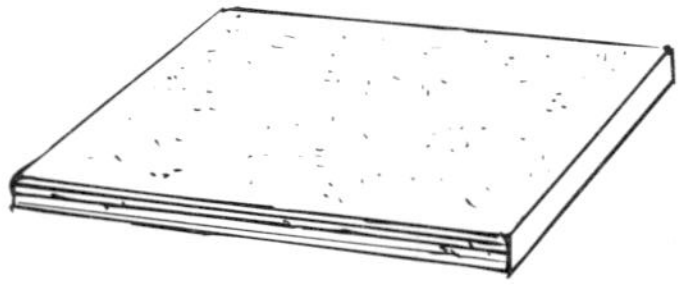

Enlarge to A3 size if required.

Electrical sort out

2

Materials can be classified as either **electrical conductors** or **electrical insulators**. An electrical conductor is a material that allows electricity to pass through it. An electrical insulator is a material that does not allow electricity to pass through it.

Electrical conductors are used to take **mains** electricity from the **power stations** where it is **generated** to the houses, schools, shops and manufacturing industries where it is used. Electrical insulators are used to prevent the flowing electricity from escaping to places where it could cause death or injury to people or present a fire risk to property.

For your own and other people's safety, it is important that you are able to classify different materials as either electrical conductors or electrical insulators.

Write the name of each of these materials in the correct column of the table. If there are any materials you are not sure about, use reference books or a CD-ROM to check, or ask a friend to help you.

plastic
gold
silk
bone
wool
brass
copper
pure water
cork
zinc
candle wax
glass
iron
silver

string
mercury
cotton
impure water
wood
leather
tin
paper
aluminium
steel
rubber
dry air
bronze
damp air

electrical conductor	electrical insulator

Look at your completed table. What do you notice about most of the materials listed in the 'electrical conductor' column?

____

1 Thermal insulation

Energy can be saved by putting **thermal insulation** in our homes, schools and places of work. Good thermal insulation materials reduce **heat loss** from inside a building, so less energy is needed to keep it warm. A badly **insulated** house can lose heat through the materials it has been made from.

The diagram below gives you a rough idea of the percentage (%) loss of heat from a building that has poorly insulated walls, windows and doors and a poorly insulated roof and floor.

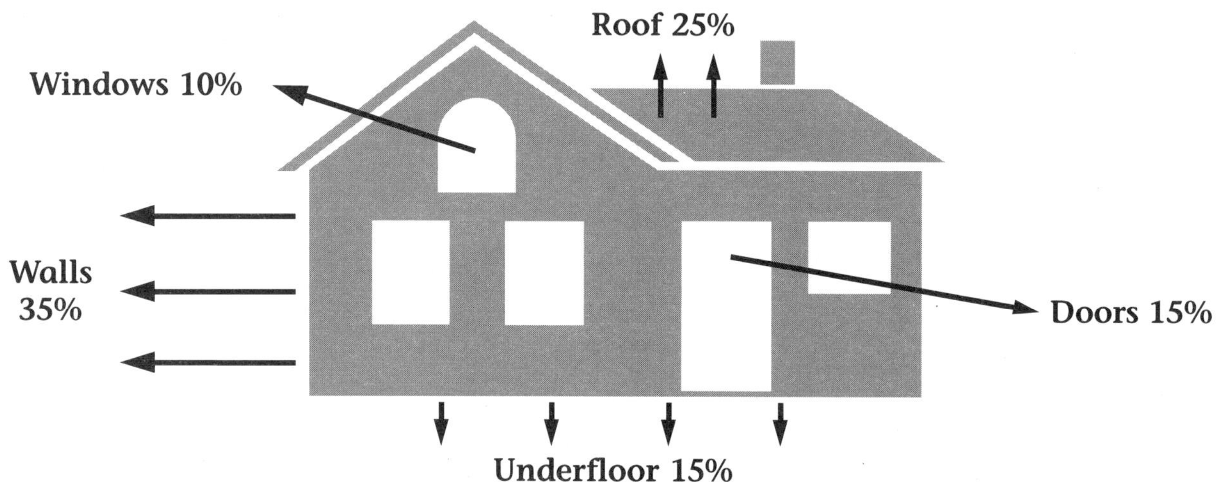

Modern building methods and the use of good **insulation** materials have helped to solve some of the thermal insulation problems that older buildings have shown. Older buildings can have their heat loss reduced by up to 50% if modern insulation methods are used.

Double glazing of windows, filling exterior cavity walls with **plastic foam** and adding loft insulation made of **fibre** and **granules** can all help to improve the thermal insulation of older buildings.

Find out about methods of thermal insulation in our homes by using reference books and CD-ROMs, or by visiting a DIY superstore and asking for leaflets.

On another sheet of paper, organise your information and write a report with the title 'Effective Home Insulation'. If appropriate, include drawings and labelled diagrams in your report.

COVER THESE INSTRUCTIONS WHEN PHOTOCOPYING.

Notes for the teacher

This page can be used either alone or in conjunction with page 81.

The investigation activity 'Keeping in heat' (page 42) is related to the science content of this page.

Thermal insulation

2

You are going to stay overnight at a friend's house. It is the middle of winter, and the house where your friend lives is old. It has poor **thermal insulation**. Even with the heating turned on full, the house loses heat to the outside very quickly.

When you arrive at your friend's house, you find that builders are working on it. They are trying to improve its thermal insulation properties.

Write an account of the things they might be doing to the house to make its thermal insulation better. If appropriate, include drawings and labelled diagrams in your report.

COVER THESE INSTRUCTIONS WHEN PHOTOCOPYING.

Notes for the teacher

The children may find a copy of page 80 a useful source of information when carrying out this activity. The investigation activity 'Keeping in heat' (page 42) is related to the science content of this page.

Safety connections

By using connecting words, we can often make two sentences into one. Examples of connecting words are: **because, so, but, unless, when, if.**

Connect these pairs of sentences together, choosing the most appropriate word from those given above. Try to use all the words at least once.
All the pairs of sentences are related to **electrical safety**. The first pair has been done for you.

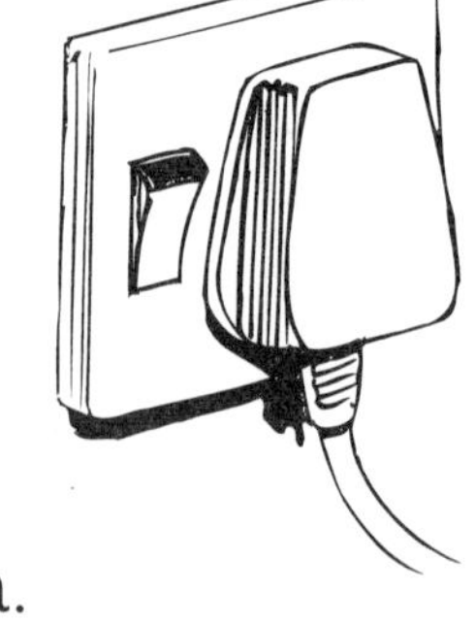

1. I never use a plug. I know that it is cracked or broken.

I never use a plug when I know that it is cracked or broken.

2. Electricity can flow through some materials. Poking things into a wall socket could electrocute you.

____

____

3. A torch battery is safe to touch. A car battery can be very dangerous.

____

4. Never change an electric light bulb. You are sure the switch is turned off.

____

5. Plastic is used to cover electrical wiring. It is a good electrical insulator.

____

6. Pushing a plug into an electrical socket with wet hands could kill you. Don't do it.

____

7. You might get an electric shock. You switch on a light with wet hands.

____

8. It is usually safe to play ball games on a playing field. You must not do so if you are close to an electricity sub-station.

____

____

____

Solids, liquids and gases

Jason sent this letter to his Grandma in Wales. She used to teach science in her younger days, and is always keen to know what Jason has been learning about in his science topics at school.

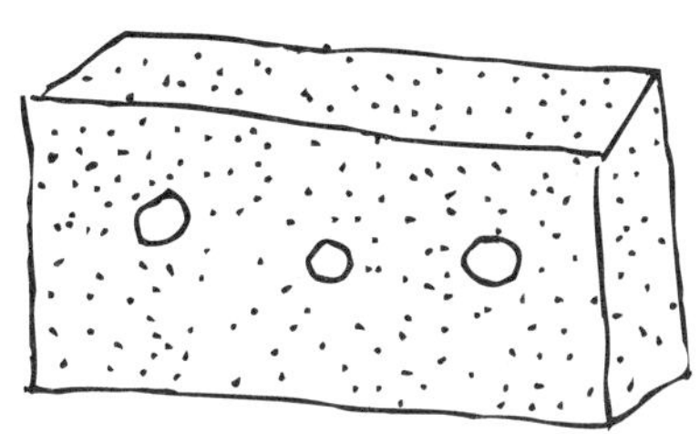

solid

liquid

16 Corncrake Avenue,
Inglewhite,
Preston,
Lancashire,
PR3 1CR.

Friday, 20th May.

Dear Grandma,

This week we have been learning about the differences between **solids**, **liquids** and **gases**. Mrs Twigg, our teacher, told us that everything is made of **matter** and that matter can be either a solid, a liquid or a gas. As you were a teacher, I expect you know that already!

Mrs Twigg also said that, under the right conditions, solids, liquids and gases can undergo a **change of state**. **Temperature** is the key to which **state** the matter is in. Let me try to explain what that means. Many solids, if heated enough, will change into liquids. Many liquids, if heated enough, will change into gases. Most of us did not realise this! Of course, the opposite is true if the process is reversed. Many gases, if cooled enough, will change into liquids. Many liquids, if cooled enough, will change into solids.

If I was actually talking to you now, I bet you would ask me what the differences are between a solid, a liquid and a gas. Well, a solid has a fixed **volume** and a fixed **shape** – for example, a brick. A liquid has a fixed volume but no definite shape – for example, milk in a carton. It takes the shape of the container it is stored in. A gas has no fixed volume or shape of its own and will spread out in all directions to fill any space that is available – for example, air in a balloon.

Am I correct? I hope so. We are having a test on Monday morning and I want to get it right.

Do you like my drawings at the top and bottom of the page? They took me ages to do.

See you at half-term.
Love,
Jason

gas in balloon

Solids, liquids and gases

1. Name the three **states** in which **matter** is found.

______________________ ______________________ ______________________

2. What is the key to the **state** that **matter** is in?

____

What will happen to many **solids** if they are heated enough?

____

What will happen to many **liquids** if they are heated enough?

____

3. Describe:

a) a **solid** ____

b) a **liquid** ____

c) a **gas** ____

4. What is the process called when a **solid** changes into a **liquid**?

____

5. What is the process called when a **liquid** changes into a **gas**?

____

6. Write a suitable ending for each of these sentences:

a) Many **gases**, when they cool, will ______________________________

b) Many **liquids**, when they cool, will ______________________________

7. Write the names of three appropriate materials in each box.

solid	liquid	gas

8. Name five **solids** that melt easily when heated by the Sun.

____________ ____________ ____________ ____________ ____________

On a blank sheet of paper, make six columns with the following headings:

solids – hard   **liquids** – runny   **gases** – odourless

solids – soft   **liquids** – viscous   **gases** – smelly

Write the names of three suitable materials in each of the columns.

Solids, liquids and gases

1. What is everything made of? ______________________

2. Write in the missing words in these sentences.

a) ______________________ is the key to which **state matter** is in.

b) Many **solids**, if heated enough, will change into ____________________

c) Many **liquids**, if heated enough, will change into ____________________

3. Connect each sentence beginning to the correct ending.

A solid has
A liquid has
A gas has

a fixed volume but no definite shape.
no fixed volume or shape of its own.
a fixed volume and shape.

4. What is the process called when a **solid** changes into a **liquid**? Circle the correct word in the list below.
What is the process called when a **liquid** changes into a **gas**? Underline the correct word in the list below.

freezing boiling melting evaporating condensing

5. Write one word in each empty box to complete this flow chart.

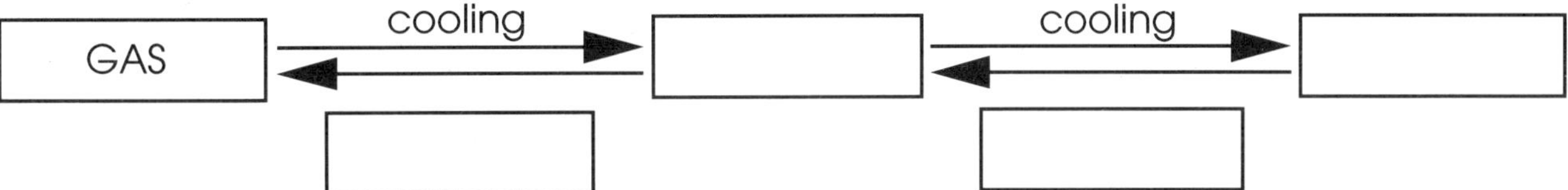

6. Tick the correct box for each material to show whether it is a **solid**, a **liquid** or a **gas**.

	solid	liquid	gas
steel			
oxygen			
milk			

	solid	liquid	gas
air			
plastic			
water			

7. Some **solid** foods melt easily when heated by the Sun. Name three of them.

____________________ ____________________ ____________________

On a blank sheet of paper, make four columns with the following headings:

solids – hard **solids** – soft **liquids** – runny **liquids** – sticky

Write the names of three suitable materials in each column.

Solids, liquids and gases round-the-class quiz

* A fizzy liquid named after a citrus fruit.	water
Rubber or plastic in a light, spongy form.	lemonade
Any material with no fixed size or shape is called a...	foam
Water in the form of a solid.	gas
Fluid provided by female mammals as food for their young.	ice
Fibres from the fleece of a sheep.	milk
Any material with a fixed size and shape is called a...	wool
We breathe this mixture of gases to stay alive.	solid
Tough, fibrous material enclosed by bark when alive.	air
A liquid fuel frequently used by commercial vehicles.	wood
A solid on the beach that can be poured like a liquid.	diesel
The most common gas in air.	sand
Any material with a fixed size but no fixed shape is called a...	nitrogen
The oxygen-bearing liquid circulating through the bodies of some animals.	liquid
A colourless, tasteless liquid with no smell.	blood

COVER THESE INSTRUCTIONS WHEN PHOTOCOPYING.

Notes for the teacher:
Photocopy this page onto card. Cut along the solid lines. Fold each card in half along the dotted line, with the text on the outside. Fasten with tape or glue. If you are working with a small group, give each child a card. If you are working with the whole class, share the cards out one between two or three. All the cards must be given out.

The child (or group) with the card marked * reads the question aloud. The child with the answer to that question reads it out, then reads out the question on the back of the card. This goes on until the first child has read out the answer on his or her card.

Solve it

The words in this crossword are all different **solids, liquids** or **gases**. The first letter of each word is provided (as a capital letter) to help you. Use lower-case letters for the rest of the word. You may need to look up some of the clues.

Clues Across

1. A whitish rock, often containing fossils.
4. A colourless, odourless, tasteless liquid.
6. A silvery-white metal.
8. The mixture of gases we breathe.
10. A soft, smooth mineral, often bought in powder form.
11. A rock from which metal can be extracted.
12. Short for the gas 'neon'.
13. A thread-like material growing out of the skin of mammals.
16. Flakes of frozen water.
18. A gas used in light bulbs.
20. Hot, liquid rock from a volcano.
21. Found under the soil layer.
22. Black drawing stick used for artwork.
23. Thin cord or rope.

Clues Down

1. The milky juice from rubber trees.
2. A rock used as a roofing material.
3. The kind of pottery made from coarse baked clay.
4. The fibres from the fleece of a sheep.
5. A strong, elastic material.
7. The gas used in illuminated signs.
9. Water falling from the clouds.
12. The most common gas in air.
14. Any kind of woven or knitted cloth.
15. The light, tough bark of a certain kind of oak tree.
17. A natural product, often called timber.
19. Molten rock inside the Earth.

The gases of the atmosphere

Read the numbered sentences at the bottom of this page. Write the sentence number in the box, and add the words in the best position to make this science text complete. You must use all the sentences.

Air is the mixture of gases that makes up the Earth's **atmosphere**.

☐ ______________________________

This means that air is roughly four-fifths nitrogen and one-fifth oxygen.

☐ ______________________________

The inert gases **argon**, **helium**, **neon**, **xenon** and **krypton** play little part in the overall working of the atmosphere, but they do have their uses.

☐ ______________________________

Without it living things would die.

☐ ______________________________

☐ ______________________________

In industry it is used for getting metals from their ores, and as a gas for cutting and welding iron and steel.

☐ ______________________________

Nitrogen is important for the healthy growth of plants, and is used in the manufacture of fertilisers.
Carbon dioxide is essential for the process of photosynthesis in green plants.

☐ ______________________________

1. In hospitals, it is given to patients with breathing difficulties.
2. By far the most important gas in the atmosphere is oxygen.
3. Oxygen has many medical and manufacturing uses.
4. It is the main gas used in fire extinguishers, and is often mixed with water to make fizzy drinks.
5. About 78% of air is **nitrogen** and 21% is **oxygen**.
6. Aircraft pilots, high-altitude balloonists and deep-sea divers also need a supply of oxygen to keep them alive.
7. About 1% of air is made up of **carbon dioxide**, **water vapour** and small quantities of other gases, called **inert** gases.

Uses of solids, liquids and gases

1. Connect each of these **solids** to its most likely use.

wood	water pipes, radiators, saucepans, drill bits, the core of electrical cables
glass	brickwork, crockery, china, ovenware
plastics	doors, furniture, window frames
ceramics	moulded items, saucepan handles, sheathing of electrical cables
metals	curtains, furnishings, clothing
fabrics	cavity wall and loft insulation, windows

2. Name three uses of **water** in your home.

a) ____________ **b)** ____________ **c)** ____________

3. Write a use for each of these **liquids**.

a) cooking oil ____________

b) paraffin ____________

c) white spirit ____________

4. Name the parts of a car where these materials might be either used or produced.

a) air ____________ **b)** carbon dioxide ____________

c) plastic ____________ **d)** lubricating oil ____________

e) coolant ____________ **f)** steel ____________

5. Circle the activities that need a special supply of **air** or **oxygen**.

submarine travel   horse riding   high-altitude ballooning   surfing

space travel   cycling   deep-sea diving

6. On another sheet of paper, list the names of five **solid** materials that can be used for building a house. Write down which part of the house each material would be used for, and why it would be used there.

The nature of matter

Everything is made of **matter**. Matter can be in a **solid**, a **liquid** or a **gaseous** form. All forms of matter are made up of very small **particles** that are constantly moving.

In a **solid**, the particles are packed closely together and remain in a fixed position relative to each other, but all the time they are **vibrating** slowly. This is why solids have a fixed shape and a fixed size.

In a **liquid**, the particles move about more **quickly**, but do not escape from each other completely. This movement allows a liquid to take on the shape of the container in which it is held, though the volume of the liquid is fixed.

In a **gas**, the particles move about very **rapidly** in all directions. Therefore a gas will expand to fill the entire space of whatever is containing it.

A change in **temperature** can result in a **change of state** for either a solid, a liquid or a gas. The diagram below illustrates how water can exist in all three states, and how it will change if there is a change in the temperature. It also shows how the movement of the water particles changes with a change in temperature.

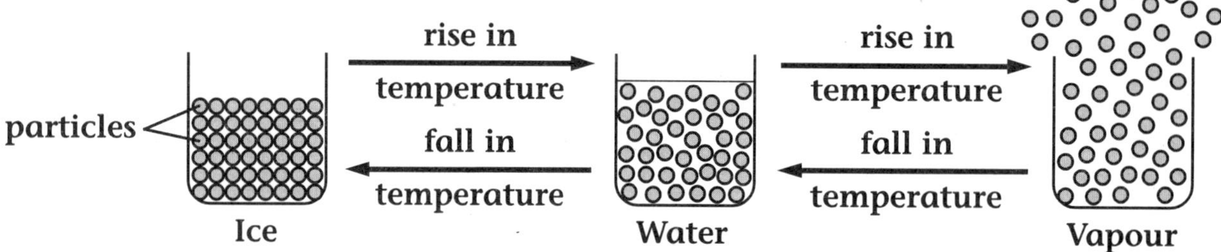

1. As in the diagram above, show how the particles of these materials would look if you could see them. **Helium** has been drawn for you.

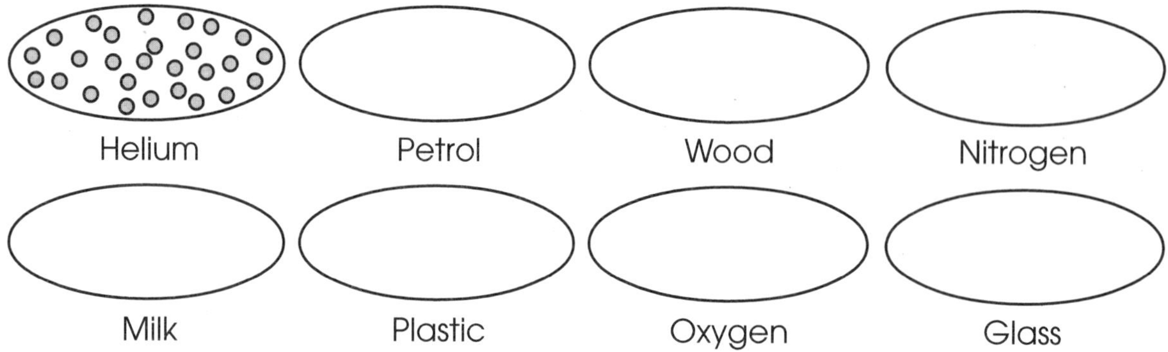

2. Look up 'kinetic theory'. (Hint: it's all about the movement energy of these particles.) Try to explain this theory in your own words. Include labelled diagrams in your explanation. Make notes from a textbook or CD-ROM before writing your final explanation.

Materials from the Earth's crust

In order to live in the modern world, humans need a wide range of materials. If these materials were not available, our lives would be completely different.

Many of the raw materials we need are obtained directly from the Earth's **crust** by processes such as **mining**, **quarrying**, **dredging** and **drilling**. Without these processes, materials such as **granite**, **limestone**, **clay**, **sand**, **gravel** and **salt** would not be available for us to use. Neither would **fossil fuels** such as **coal**, **oil** and **natural gas**.

Many materials extracted from the Earth's crust cannot be used in their natural state. However, after simple processing, many of them become very useful. Quarried rock, for example, is broken into smaller pieces; dredged sand is washed; and gravel fragments are sorted by size.

The Earth's crust also provides us with important raw materials that have to go through quite complicated processes before they can be used. For example:

- **glass** is made from **sand** and other **minerals**
- **metals** are refined from their **ores**
- **coke** is manufactured from **coal**
- firing **clay** makes **ceramics** such as **bricks** and **tiles**
- **crude oil** is used to make **paraffin** and **petrol**.

Just think about all the different types of materials that come from the Earth, and their hundreds of uses. You'll soon realise just how important the Earth's crust is for providing materials that we 'cannot do without'.

Materials from the Earth's crust

1. Name four processes that enable us to obtain raw materials directly from the Earth's **crust**.

______________________ ______________________

______________________ ______________________

2. What are the three main kinds of **fossil fuels**?

______________ ______________ ______________

3. What simple process can be carried out on each of these materials to make it become very useful?

a) quarried rock ______________________

b) dredged sand ______________________

c) gravel ______________________

4. Answer these questions in complete sentences.

a) What is **glass** made from?

____

b) What are **metals** refined from?

____

c) From which product is **coke** manufactured?

____

d) Which two products, among others, can be made from **crude oil**?

____

5. Name three rocks not mentioned in the text that are extracted from the Earth's **crust** by either **mining** or **quarrying**.

______________ ______________ ______________

6. Which rock in particular is quarried for cement production?

____

Talk with friends about products, made from materials in the Earth's crust, that you 'cannot do without'. Find out more about the origin of the materials from which these products are made, and write a report.

Materials from the Earth's crust

1. Circle the names of the four processes that allow raw materials to be obtained directly from the Earth's **crust**.

quarrying melting condensing mining

evaporating dredging drilling freezing

2. Tick the words that are the names of **fossil fuels**.

burning	☐	natural gas	☐	wood	☐
oil	☐	central heating	☐	coal	☐

3. Connect each material to a simple way in which it can be processed after being taken out of the Earth's **crust**.

quarried rock		washed
dredged sand		broken into smaller pieces
gravel		sorted by size

4. Fill in the missing words in these sentences.

a) **Glass** is made from ____________ and other ____________ .

b) **Metals** are refined from their ____________ .

c) ____________ is manufactured from **coal**.

d) **Paraffin** and **petrol** are made from ____________ ____________ .

5. Circle the names of three raw materials that are extracted from the Earth's **crust** by either **mining** or **quarrying**.

marble timber slate rubber sandstone

6. Circle the name of the rock that is quarried for making cement.

sand gravel limestone boulders granite

Talk with friends about products, made from materials in the Earth's crust, that you 'cannot do without'. Use reference books or CD-ROMs to find out more about the origin of the materials from which these products are made.

Power from the Earth

You will need: scissors, glue and a large sheet of paper or card.

The paragraphs in this text are in the correct order, but the sentences in each paragraph are mixed up.

What to do:

1. Cut out the sentences in each paragraph.

2. Rearrange the sentences so that they make sense, then paste them in the correct order on a sheet of paper or card.

Paragraph 1

As a group, these materials are called **fossil fuels** because they have formed over a long period of time from organic remains, and are effectively **non-renewable**.

The energy stored within them came originally from the Sun.

Three of the most useful fuels that we get from the Earth's **crust** are **coal**, **oil** and **natural gas**.

Fossil fuels, when **burned**, provide us with **heat**, **light** and **power**.

Paragraph 2

The build-up of this gas in the Earth's atmosphere is thought to be responsible for the process known as **global warming**.

Coal is formed from dead plant material that has been decaying slowly over millions of years.

As well as providing useful energy, burning coal unfortunately releases large quantities of a gas called **carbon dioxide** into the **atmosphere**.

Much of the coal used in the world is burned in **power stations**.

Paragraph 3

Oil and natural gas are formed from the remains of small sea creatures that lived millions of years ago.

As with coal, when these fuels are burned (either in power stations or in our homes, schools, factories and vehicles), carbon dioxide is released into the atmosphere.

These creatures, over a long period of time, have decayed to form deposits of either oil (a liquid) or natural gas (methane).

Useful materials from the Earth's crust

Link parts of sentences from each box to form complete sentences. Write out each sentence. Don't forget to punctuate the sentences correctly. One has been done for you.

Slate is a smooth, hard rock	drilled from deep wells	and is used as a building stone.
Sandstone feels rough to the touch,	spread on icy road surfaces in winter	and can be eaten when purified.
Oil is a mineral deposit,	that can be split into flat pieces	and used as a solid fuel in power stations.
Chalk is a fine-grained,	is made of sand packed tightly together	and often found in conjunction with natural gas.
Coal is a hard black mineral,	soft and crumbly rock	and used as a roofing material.
Rock salt is obtained from below ground level,	formed from decayed plant materials	that can be used in the manufacture of cement.

1. Slate is a smooth, hard rock that can be split into flat pieces and used as a roofing material.

2. ______________________________

3. ______________________________

4. ______________________________

5. ______________________________

6. ______________________________

Find out more information about the materials listed above. Arrange what you find out into a short talk to present to the rest of the class.

Crusty wordsearch

In this wordsearch are the names of twelve different **materials** that are extracted from the Earth's **crust**. Clues and the first letter of each name are given. You will have to search in all directions, including diagonally. Draw a line through each word in the wordsearch when you find it.

Clues

1. A hard, blackish mineral that is burned to supply heat (c).
2. A yellowish metal of very high value (g).
3. An ore or other material obtained by mining (m).
4. A soft and crumbly white rock (c).
5. A mixture of coarse sand and small stones (g).
6. A reddish-brown metal (c).
7. A very hard kind of stone that can make sparks when struck against steel (f).
8. A hard mineral occurring in various forms (q).
9. A lightweight silvery metal (a).
10. A sticky material that becomes hard when baked (c).
11. A very hard, brilliant and precious stone (d).
12. The group of solids that are good thermal and electrical conductors (m).

h	r	i	c	h	a	l	k	i	c	j	z
d	l	o	g	a	l	a	r	e	n	i	m
j	a	g	t	r	u	k	f	s	i	o	y
l	h	s	a	g	m	l	u	m	l	y	a
t	n	z	q	n	i	o	p	l	e	f	l
h	k	q	f	n	n	y	m	r	b	j	c
v	u	z	t	g	i	u	t	e	a	s	r
d	v	t	w	f	u	s	l	a	t	e	m
y	p	r	m	b	m	x	d	o	p	f	p
g	r	a	v	e	l	w	a	p	x	b	x
c	z	u	b	k	d	n	o	m	a	i	d
n	q	q	v	e	l	c	c	w	c	d	e

Choose three words from the ones you have found. On another sheet of paper, write each word in a separate sentence that shows you understand the meaning of the word.